"This fascinating, fictionalized memo[…] [illegible] moving events of a deaf woman's life. Zhila Shirazi not only survives but rises above anti-Semitic persecution in Iran and personal tragedies as she finds a new home and family in America. Her widower, author Thal, skillfully uses fiction techniques to give her story immediacy. This fluidly written and upbeat memoir should enjoy wide appeal."

Jacqueline Diamond, *USA Today* bestselling author of the "Safe Harbor Medical" series

"*The Lip Reader* by Michael Thal is well-researched and well-written with a wonderful variety of characters, places, and events. Zhila's bravery, dedication, and determination are beautifully captured. I especially enjoyed the smooth flow of the story and the constant pace throughout, following the lives of Zhila, her friends, and her family. The novel is well-edited and easy to read with vivid descriptions and scenes which make it easy for the reader to form a visual of the story. Overall, a thoroughly enjoyable novel, highly recommended."

Natalie Soine, *Readers' Favorite*

"I was lucky enough to be one of first to read *The Lip Reader* by Michael Thal. It was a privilege and an honor to get to know the heroine, Zhila Shirazi, as she came to life for me through Michael's writing. *The Lip Reader*, based on a true story, is heartwarming and inspiring. Readers will fall in love with Zhila as she maneuvers bravely through her often, difficult life. Kudos to Michael for sharing her story, a story everyone should read."

Jeanne Bannon, author of *Invisible*

"A poignant portrayal of Zhila Shirazi, who embodied the word 'resilient'. Zhila was truly a person who gave more than she received and a beautiful example of compassion in action. Author Michael Thal has created a first-person account of Zhila's life, giving the reader a humbling opportunity to walk with, and learn from, this amazing person."

Nancy Wood, author of the "The Shelby McDougall Mysteries"

"This story is a powerful reminder that truth sometimes can indeed be stranger than fiction! It would be difficult for even the most hard-hearted to go through *The Lip Reader* without at least being emotional and feeling moist in the eyes. There are equally lots of witty lines interspersed throughout the course of the book that would literally have you rolling on the ground with laughter. *The Lip Reader* is a masterpiece you wouldn't want to miss for anything!"

Official Review, *ILoveUniqueBooks.com* (4 out of 5 stars)

"*The Lip Reader* is the memoir of a deceased deaf woman, shining a light onto Persian culture and the obvious and subtle effects of deafness. Some of the events covered are dramatic enough to feature in any novel, others are commonplace, part of almost any life, but all are told with a refreshing clearness that made me want to read on. If you want an enjoyable, interesting read, and would like to see a pathway to becoming a better person yourself, you should invest in Michael's writing, including *The Lip Reader*."

Dr. Bob Rich, author of *Hit and Run* and *Guardian Angel*

"Michael Thal's *The Lip Reader* is an inspiring tale that follows the journey of a deaf woman, Zhila, as she struggles through her childhood In Iran and eventually immigrates to America. She has a wonderful story to tell, and Michael Thal has written it beautifully. The pace is steady, and the words are direct. You'll enjoy this book if you like extraordinary dramas. It also makes one understand, if only a little, the life of a deaf person. I recommend this book for anyone who enjoyed *Terms of Endearment* or *The Grapes of Wrath.* Sometimes tales of tragedy are needed to bring us more understanding. An excellent read."

Rod Little, author of O*n Gravedigger Road*

The Lip Reader

Michael Thal

Published by Paper Angel Press
paperangelpress.com

ISBN 978-1-953469-83-0 (Trade Paperback)

10 9 8 7 6 5 4 3 2 1

FIRST EDITION

DEDICATION

In loving memory of Jila.
I miss you every day.

"It's not what you get in life, it's what you give back that truly defines you."

Zhila Shirazi

ACKNOWLEDGEMENTS

AFTER MY ZHILA PASSED AWAY in the winter of 2015, grief enveloped me more than I could have ever imagined. To move beyond the daily crying binges, I decided to put her story on paper. This took four years and the help of a lot of wonderful people.

During the early stages of research, I want to thank Azin David and Dr. Juliet Hananian for their insights into Iranian culture and family history.

Every month I took a freshly written chapter to my writing group, The San Fernando Critters (SFC). They showed me a chapter's strengths and weaknesses and what I needed to do to improve its content. Thank you so much SFC members Anne Mcgee, Anjali Amit, and Rachel Brachman. Though Susan Schader left our group for a new life in Maryland, she insisted I send her copies of my chapters to which she provided her valuable input. And while I'm discussing Alpha readers, I don't want to skip my good friend, Jeanne Bannon-Repole who looked over every chapter I rewrote after my writing group's input.

Once the novel was complete, I handed it over to Beta readers Joe Bock and Koren Jozana. From their comments I decided I needed an editor. I reached out to my ASL interpreter and friend, Jan Seeley, for an editor that was sensitive to deaf issues. Unbeknownst to me, Jan included editing in her resume. She was a perfect choice and did a marvelous job chopping away at excess verbiage as she tightened up the novel.

I would like to also thank the people at Paper Angel Press, especially managing editor Steven Radecki who is 100% enthused by *The Lip Reader* and will guide it to success. When I mentioned to Steven the name of a very talented illustrator, April Klein, he agreed to hire her to design and illustrate the book cover for my novel. Now that's supportive!

A few writing friends agreed to read and review an advanced copy of *The Lip Reader.* For their efforts and faith in my writing talent I want to thank Nancy Wood, author of the Shelby McDougall Mysteries, Jacqueline Diamond, author of the Safe Harbor Medical series, Rod Little, author of *When Butterflies Scream*, and the very talented psychologist/author/professional grandfather Dr. Bob Rich, author of *Guardian Angel.*

Preface

FOUR MONTHS BEFORE HER DEATH, Zhila noticed a suspicious-looking mole on my back and made me promise to have it checked out.

Devastated by her dying and subsequent death, I precariously survived the first year without her, but completely forgot about the mole. The subject strangely came up again at the unveiling of her headstone. Zhila's brother, a medical doctor, noticed a different mole, this time on my face and cautioned me to get it looked at. A theme seemed to be emerging.

The dermatologist looked at the mole my brother-in-law discovered and said, "That's nothing." I directed him to the mole Zhila noticed on my back and he said, "Now, that is something!" The biopsy revealed it was cancerous and I was secretly pleased, hoping to join my soul mate. Adjusting to life without her had proven to be more difficult than I ever imagined was possible. It was a long surgery, but I survived.

To get control of the grieving process, I needed to find a way to get past my paralysis and honor Zhila's memory instead of being mired in my sorrow. I began to document and organize all of the stories she had told me of her life in Iran and then the United States. I had won an award for an essay of one of her stories, so I decided to weave them all together into a novel based on the true events of her life.

The names you will find in her story have been altered for privacy concerns, and events have been embellished for continuity and literary considerations, but I hope Zhila Shirazi's story touches you as much as she touched me.

Michael Thal

INTRODUCTION

MY NAME IS ZHILA SHIRAZI, grandniece of Rabbi Yousef Kohani Hamdani. I try to impress my Jewish friends with that piece of trivia, but only the Orthodox pay it any mind.

I suffer some medical problems, but my most troublesome condition is deafness, which I have coped with since I was three years old. I say "coped with" because, in my country of Iran, a disability is a curse. The primary way that I cope is through lip reading and I rely heavily on that to relate to the world. Lip reading requires direct eye contact that sometimes can make people feel uncomfortable, so added to that already difficult task is the ongoing enlightenment of others. It can be exhausting.

I am the oldest of four children. Solomon, my father, owns a small pharmacy and my mother, Sara, cares for our family. I have two younger sisters, Zandra and Zanna, and our sweet little brother, Ziggy. We are a very close family that also includes my mother's sister, my aunt Sabra, and her children.

I once asked my mother, "Why do we all have the same first letter of our names?"

Maamaan answered, "I want my children to feel as if they are a unit."

"How can a letter be a unit?" I quizzed her.

She thought for a moment and offered this example:

"Your clothes are handed down to Zandra and hers to Zanna. Having the same initial makes it more efficient to label your school clothes; I only have to label them once. You are all my sweet little Z's. Each separate and special but also a unit."

Thinking I would stump her, I said, "But what about Ziggy? He does not wear our clothes."

"Of course not," she said, "But he is our sweetest little Z and the rest of the unit looks out for him."

That was how I learned the importance of family.

My story begins in Tehran …

BOOK ONE

TEHRAN, IRAN

1

WHEN I WAS NINE, I read an article in the *Ettela'at*, our newspaper, about an audiologist fitting a deaf child with hearing aids. The caption in Farsi under the photo of the little girl with tears rolling down her face read: "Oh my! I can hear my voice!"

That was the moment I decided I must have hearing aids, too. I lobbied my mother, showing her the article, but she just smiled and nodded. Report card day bolstered my case, showing poor progress in math. My parents wanted to hire a tutor, but I suggested they invest in hearing aids instead. I said, "If I could hear the teacher, I would do a lot better in class. I would rather have hearing aids."

I kept nagging them over months, never missing an opportunity to make my case. I pounced one evening while they were relaxed and least expected it, as Papa sat in his leather lounger smoking and Maamaan crocheted a blanket. Taking a stance on the Persian rug between them, I clapped my hands to secure their attention and announced, "I cannot hear my voice and I do not have the slightest idea what your voices sound like. My grades in school suffer because when the teacher turns her back, I miss everything!" I crossed my arms stubbornly and stared intently at them. "I want hearing aids!"

Maamaan never looked up and continued crocheting "Go to bed. It is late. Your father and I will discuss it."

I understood why my parents wanted to turn a blind eye to the problem. In our culture it was not safe to be different. Being Jewish in a Muslim country was difficult enough, but if your child had a disability, you kept that fact very private. People with disabilities in mid-twentieth century Iran were considered tragic and pitiful. Those afflicted were seen as unfit or feeble-minded and incapable of contributing to society. Their worth was only valued as entertainment in a circus sideshow or as objects of scorn. Many disabled individuals were forced to undergo sterilization so as not to pass disabling genes to their offspring.

I could appreciate that my parents wanted my deafness to remain a secret; hearing aids would be stark evidence of my inferiority. They feared ridicule from the community for their inability to sire healthy, normal children. It was safer and much less complicated to pretend all was well, until the consequences began to force the issue.

I arrived home from school, bleeding, crying, and dripping wet.

"My God, Zhila! What happened?" Maamaan dropped her duster on the living room table and rushed to my side.

I kicked off my boots near the front door and ran to my room.

"Nothing!" I slammed the door behind me. Maamaan waited a few minutes, and then knocked softly on my bedroom door.

"Go away!"

She ignored my drama, came in and sat down next to me on the bed. "Let me look at that," she said pointing to the wound on my head caked with dried blood. "I need to clean it." She placed the first aid kit on the night table, wet a ball of cotton with antiseptic, and said, "This will sting."

As she worked, Maamaan asked, "Who did this to you?"

"My teacher!" I broke down and cried in her arms.

When the shaking and sobs subsided, Maamaan gently moved me to arm's length, "Tell me what happened."

"We were working on a math problem and Mrs. Saidi's back was to the class, writing on the board as she spoke to us. I had no idea that she had called on me to come up to solve the problem.

"She turned around, her face beet red, looking at me with fire in her eyes. 'Miss Shirazi, when I speak to you, I expect a response!' She turned back to the board and put up another problem. In her fury, even I could hear the scraping chalk echo in the room.

"Mrs. Saidi turned around again her face even redder and screamed at me so hard stray spittle took flight and landed in my hair."

Maamaan put a Band-Aid on the side of my temple and closed the first aid kit. "What happened next?"

"She ordered me to stand by the door and then said something with her back to me and a few students laughed and then she asked why I was still standing there. I did not know what she was talking about, and I was so embarrassed standing there completely confused. Mrs. Saidi grabbed the pencil from behind her ear, lunged at me and gouged it into my head and said, 'That should wake you up, you stupid Jew, now get out of my class and don't come back until you learn respect.'

"So, I stood outside under an awning with the wind and rain blowing in my face waiting."

I sneezed and Maamaan ordered me to get out of my damp clothes and take a shower.

As I undressed, I said, "If I had hearing aids, this would not have happened."

Maamaan got off the bed and held me in her arms. Then she pulled away and said, "For your twelfth birthday, we will see an audiologist."

That was three years away, but I had a delightful shower.

2

I NEVER LOOKED FORWARD TO A BIRTHDAY with more excitement than my twelfth. I had waited three long years and now it was Operation Hearing Aids!

As usual, I walked to school with cousin Parry, Aunt Sabra's daughter. This school year was so much better than Mrs. Saidi's class, not only because Parry was in my room, but Miss Avedisian, our teacher, was really kind. She believed in teaching using the philosophy of the school's Christian founder — a righteous woman who wanted to educate young girls, no matter what their background or religion.

Miss Avedisian was aware of my deafness because Parry told her. On the first day of class, Parry stopped at our teacher's desk while I stood waiting at the door. She whispered something to her and Miss Avedisian looked over at me and smiled.

That was all it took. Thanks to Parry, Miss Avedisian never spoke with her back to me. When she asked me a question, she looked directly at me and spoke slowly enough to make sure I understood. My grades skyrocketed and finally I was happy.

School had been dismissed early that Wednesday afternoon as I ran home with Parry in my wake. At a busy intersection, my cousin caught up to me and asked, "What is the big rush?"

As the noisy traffic sped by, I said, "I told you already. Maamaan promised me hearing aids. We get them today!"

As the light changed, I dashed off knowing I was being terribly rude, but I was so exhilarated I had no time for manners, and left Parry at the corner shaking her head.

I burst through the front door, sweaty with a blue scarf tangled haphazardly around my neck. Maamaan scowled, "Go take a shower, change clothes and we will go."

"But we will be late," I whined.

Maamaan stood with her hands on her hips, her apron concealing her pregnant belly. "We have an hour, plenty of time, now go."

Supergirl could not have showered and dressed faster.

I walked quickly ahead of Maamaan and kept turning to face her, urging her to walk faster. She waddled contentedly behind me, making no attempt at all to satisfy my coaxing. From Darband Street, near Sa'dabad Palace, home to the Shah, we headed east on Tajik, and entered a medical center at the end of the block. Maamaan filled out the requisite forms, handing them to the receptionist, who puffed at her bangs to get them out of her eyes.

"Dr. Mohammadi will be with you shortly."

I was too excited to sit. Soon I would be able to hear! I imagined all the sounds I would hear: music, my teacher's voice, the new baby crying … the possibilities were endless. While we waited, I studied a framed drawing of an ear on the wall, labeled with the *Ear Canal*, *Middle Ear*, *Inner Ear*, and *Eustachian Tube*. The receptionist interrupted my scrutiny and I helped Maamaan struggle to her feet.

Dr. Mohammadi had bushy eyebrows, and a kind face with a chipped front tooth that distracted from his bright smile. "Welcome, young lady," he said offering his hand.

I shook it enthusiastically and blurted out, "I need hearing aids!"

He offered my mother a seat near his desk. "For that we will need to do some tests." He spoke slowly and distinctly, just like Miss Avedisian. He escorted me to the soundproof booth. "First we will do a Pure Tone test. You sit on that chair and place those headphones over your ears. If you hear a sound, raise your left hand. Okay?"

I nodded and eagerly entered the booth. Once the headphones were in place, a loud beep assaulted my right ear and my hand enthusiastically shot up. Another beep, up went my hand, then fewer, then nothing. I did better with the left ear although most sounds were faint as if from far away, but still I was encouraged. I kept the headphones on for the next test where he instructed me to repeat the word that I heard. Again, my right ear failed completely and words made little sense in the left.

He performed a few more tests, sticking instruments in my ears then looking at his gadgets and meters and charts, then jotted down notes. When he finished analyzing the results, he informed us that I had a profound loss in my right ear, and in my better ear on the left, I had a severe loss. We quizzed him about the significance of that and what was the next step.

The technical explanation went over my head and I almost lost all hope when he told us there was no remedy for my right ear; no hearing aid could help. I perked up again when he said that with an aid on my left, I might understand some speech.

"The meningitis you had as a child destroyed the hair-like structures in your ears, necessary for the complicated process of hearing and understanding sound.

You can hear sounds on the order of a fire engine siren or a school bell, but cannot comprehend human speech. But I see that you have compensated by learning to read lips. I rarely see anyone with your level of hearing loss to be so skilled at that; it is very impressive. It was helpful that you were born with hearing so your brain was able to process language for a time before the meningitis destroyed it."

"When can I get the hearing aid for my left ear?"

"The hearing aid you need is only made by an American company." He went over to a cabinet and pulled out a box showing me what it looked like and how it worked.

"Can I try it?"

"Sorry, this device will not work for you. It is not powerful enough."

Maamaan asked, "What is the price of the one she would need?"

I was so excited about getting a hearing aid that cost never occurred to me. I held my breath afraid of his answer.

Dr. Mohammadi turned his head away from me and spoke to my mother.

Maamaan gasped, stood up thanking the doctor for his time and briskly exited his office signaling me to follow. She walked stone-faced, down Tajik Road heading home.

I ran ahead of her and then turned walking backward facing her. "Can I get the hearing aid?"

"No, it's too expensive."

"I will get a job! I will help pay for it."

Maamaan found the energy to walk vigorously past me.

I screamed, "Maamaan, I want a hearing aid!"

She did not respond; she just walked faster.

"Please, Maamaan!"

She crossed the street straight for home, the bottom corners of her long winter coat flapping in the cold wind. I caught up with her and screamed, "Maamaan! I want to hear music and laughter. I hate being so different! You do not want people to know! You are afraid they will gossip that your daughter is defective! God forbid they see a hearing aid and realize I am deaf!"

Pedestrians stared and people stuck their heads out of windows to see what the commotion was about. Maamaan halted in mid-stride, shaking, her face flushed with anger. She turned toward me and I felt the bitter sting of her open hand against my face.

"NEVER speak of this again."

My mother had never struck me, and I had never seen her so angry. I realized this subject must run much deeper than I realized. I had touched a tender nerve creating this dramatic response from this person that I no longer recognized.

I trailed behind her covering my face with my hands sobbing in bitter disillusionment.

3

"YOU WERE BORN HERE in this room twelve years ago," Aunt Sabra said.

"Yes, I remember. You told me that when Zandra was born."

Aunt Sabra, Maamaan's oldest sister, readied her midwifery implements and placed them on the mahogany dresser disturbing my mother's sleep. Her eyes fluttered open and my aunt placed a damp cloth on her pained brow.

When Aunt Sabra told me that I was old enough now to assist her in the birth, I was so excited. But as the time came closer, my excitement turned to nerves. She assured me she would guide me and not to worry. We arranged for Ziggy to go next door to play with his friend; Zandra went to Aunt Rebecca's and, naturally, my father was at the pharmacy working.

I knelt on the Persian rug on the opposite side of the bed so that I could read my aunt's plump, red lips as she spoke to my mother. "The birth of this child will be powerful. I sense it is a girl and one day she will become a healer."

Maamaan smiled. During her pregnancy I had asked her why she refused to have her baby in a hospital. She said, "Having my child at home is empowering and spiritual, making it a better environment to bond with my baby, creating a better relationship with my child."

"I must have been born somewhere else," I teased.

She scowled and pushed me away, still annoyed with me over the public display in the street we had four months earlier. She had not forgiven me yet for making her strike me to put an end to my tantrum. I had forgiven her, but I would never forget that day.

Maamaan's sudden high-pitched shriek brought me back into the present. Aunt Sabra placed a pillow against her back and rolled her onto her side to better position her body. "Deep breaths, Sara. Trust your body's instincts, breathe again … now rest." I followed Aunt Sabra into the kitchen, where she prepared tea, heaping a stack of Koloochehs, her heavenly cookies, on a plate.

"I love your outfit, Aunt Sabra. It is simple but so elegant. Where did you buy it?"

"I bought the fabric at the Grand Bazaar and made it myself."

I stared in wonder, "You are so gifted and do such beautiful work." I took a bite of cookie and changed the subject, "Would not Maamaan be more comfortable having the baby in a hospital where she could get medicine?"

Aunt Sabra shook her head emphatically, her thick hair bouncing on her shoulders. "Iranian hospitals view birth as high risk and use technological intervention. As a midwife, I know that pregnancy and birth are natural processes. As a Jew, I believe a new life is precious and should be given every possible blessing to start a strong life. Why should a sweet, baby girl start life surrounded by such inhospitable attitudes?"

I was so curious, "How do you know she is having a girl?"

"From experience and intuition, one gets a feel for it and picks up clues. I have been a midwife for many years and have helped many women birth at home." She plucked a Koloocheh from the plate and dunked it into her tea. "Women in labor do not receive much attention in the hospital. Their husbands are not involved and family is not allowed. At home she is more comfortable, we can support her, and she can experience the birth the way she prefers. Pain is a natural part of the process."

At that moment, a distressing howl echoed from the bedroom. Aunt Sabra put down her cup and darted out of the kitchen and down the long corridor toward her sister.

"That is natural?" I mumbled sarcastically scurrying off behind her, "I will definitely have my babies in a hospital."

Maamaan's breathing came in agitated short gasps, but with soothing coaching from Sabra, she calmed and her breathing became deep and purposeful. Her dark hair clung to her sweaty, contorted face as she screamed again.

"Do something!" I shrieked.

Aunt Sabra stared at me with her intense, dark eyes and calmly said, "You are to be quiet and do as I say or leave this room." Then her attention went back to my mother, "Sara, you are fully dilated. It is time to push. Zhila, let her squeeze your hand it will help her."

"*Pedarsag! Keer bokhor!*" My mother cursed, pushed, and nearly broke my hand.

Sabra reminded her to breathe, "Now, short breaths, Sara, short breaths. That's right. Now push!" Aunt Sabra tapped me, to get my attention, "Go to the foot of the bed and prepare to catch the baby."

Catch the baby? I thought to myself. *What if I drop her?* I am going to be the first to hold my new sister. I prayed, *please God do not allow me to do anything wrong.* Within minutes, the top of a dark, little head popped out from its hiding place, then one last push and a wet, wrinkled baby plopped into my arms. Our sobs of joy and relief mingled with the protesting howls from this beautiful little creature were so loud that even I could hear them.

"You were right, Sabra, it is a girl!"

Sabra snipped and tied the cord. "Now place your sister on your mother's chest."

Carefully I handed the baby to my mother who had opened her arms in an adoring welcome. Sabra walked around to the other side of the bed and helped Maamaan to a sitting position supported by pillows as they guided the baby to nurse. The room went quiet.

I stared lovingly at this miracle who we called Zanna. Instinctively I knew this tiny, pink baby, so tightly swaddled, would one day become my best friend.

4

IN OUR HOME, DINNERTIME WAS QUIET TIME. Papa wanted to eat his meal in peace, so, on the evenings when we were all eating at the table together, discussions were not permitted. That worked to my advantage since it was really dizzying to lip read and follow multiple, simultaneous conversations.

On an evening that I had some news to share, Papa was working late at the pharmacy and Maamaan was busy feeding the baby, so I was waiting for the right opportunity to talk to Zandra. Ziggy was fidgety and wanted to be excused, devouring three beef kabobs, then arguing with Maamaan about leaving his dreadful broccoli.

Maamaan held Zanna over her shoulder, patting her to encourage a burp and, when it presented itself, it was so loud that Zandra and I broke into hysterical laughter. Ziggy took full advantage of the diversion and scooted away from the table and out of sight.

"Zhila, why are you so happy tonight?" Zandra asked.

"I made a new friend today at school. I left geography class and was hurrying to Algebra when I saw two girls heading for a collision. One was walking slowly, looking down reading a book, and the other walked while tracing the wall with one hand as she crept along.

"They bumped into each other and books scattered everywhere. The other girls in the hallway pointed and made fun of them and walked away laughing instead of helping, which really irritated me.

"The book reader yelled at the wall hugger. 'What is wrong with you? Watch where you are going!'

I interrupted and said, 'One could ask the same of you,' then picked up her book and shoved it at her. The wall hugger was having trouble finding her books, so I gathered them up for her and coaxed her to stop crying. I realized she was in my Algebra class, so we introduced ourselves and headed down the hall to class. After Algebra, we had lunch together and got to know each other.

"Her name is Goli and she is visually impaired. That was why she has trouble walking the hallway."

The wheels in Zandra's head began to turn and then she smiled. "Sounds like you two would make a great team; she can be your ears and you can be her eyes."

Zandra's prediction proved to be truer than she ever imagined. We became very close friends and developed a unique relationship that evolved quite organically.

I never told Goli about my deafness and she never asked. She astutely observed that if she looked away while speaking to me, she always had to repeat herself. I would read text to her if it was too small for her to see, and she would repeat what people said if I missed it. We always had each other's back.

One beautiful spring day, Goli and I were strolling along Sajjad Road, toward her house. Sajjad is a very busy, tree-lined thoroughfare with so many lanes there is no room for sidewalks.

As is the custom, we walked in the street. I took the outside position, nearer to traffic, and Goli took the inside so that she could use the curb to maneuver more easily.

It is very difficult to lip read when walking side-by-side, requiring tremendous concentration. We were chatting about some boy she liked in her neighborhood, and I was focusing on her mouth from the side, paying little attention to anything else.

Suddenly, I felt an abrupt tug on my right arm and fell hard on the concrete. Goli had pulled me away from the traffic as a car coming up behind us honked and whizzed by, nearly hitting me. I lay on the ground in a stupor as Goli shook her fist, cursing the driver very loudly in Arabic.

"He almost hit you! Are you okay?" she asked.

I brushed the dirt off my school uniform and nodded, "I think so. Thanks for saving me."

These are the hazards of deafness. I live in a world of constant, watchful caution. I must be observant because I cannot hear the sounds of danger. On another occasion, Goli was not with me and the result was disastrous.

5

I STRUGGLED TO REIN IN MY PINK SCARF to retain my unruly, dark hair, tossed every which way on this blustery spring day. I was walking home along Hashemi Street, one of the oldest streets in Tehran, located in District 10. It was the most populous area of Tehran's twenty-two municipal districts. I always walked this route home from Goli's because it was so beautiful. Old stately mansions were set back off the tree-lined block with expansive lawns stretching to the street surrounded by brick walls or ornate fences.

Fighting against the wind, I held onto my book bag with one hand and tried hopelessly to hang on to my scarf with the other. The wind won the duel snatching my scarf and depositing it at the roadside several meters in front of me. I rushed to pick it up, but by the time I bent over to grab it, the wind seized it again and it took flight as if it had grown wings. I chased it along the road, finally catching up and halting it with my boot. As I leaned over to retrieve my delinquent scarf, something clipped me from behind and violently shoved me into the muddy gutter.

I do not know how long I lay unconscious, but I struggled to get my bearings as my daze started to lift, to make sense of what had happened. I mustered the strength to push myself to my knees and a jolt of pain assaulted me and I nearly passed out again. If I could just get to Papa's pharmacy, he would know what to do, but that was going to require a herculean effort.

My father owned Farvardin Pharmacy, a small drugstore on Daneshgah Jang Boulevard at the edge of District 10. It was a busy shop that provided our family with everything we needed to support our lifestyle. It was only a block away, but it felt as hopeless as if I were hiking to the Black Sea. I had no idea how I was going to get up to start the trek.

My first attempt sent excruciating pain traveling from my back down my leg, forcing me to stop. At least now I had an idea of where the pain was centered and nothing seemed to be broken. I spotted a tree in front of a wrought iron fence surrounding one of the beautiful mansions and decided that I must get there. I had no subsequent recall as to how I made it to the tree, but I plastered myself against it, relieving a bit of the pain. I chose an incremental sequence of targets, somehow keeping myself upright as I reached each one. As I closed in on the familiar corner where our small pharmacy stood, relief washed over me. If I could just cross the street, lift my feet up over the curb, and get to the heavy glass doors, I would be safe.

Gasping for air in between searing bursts of pain, I made it to the doors. At the same moment, a middle-aged man rushed out, clutching his recent purchase, bumping into me. Agonizing pain ripped through my body and, praise HaShem, I blacked out.

When my eyes fluttered open, I found myself on the couch in the back room of the pharmacy looking up into Papa's eyes. He stared down at me with an expression of grave concern and gently asked, "What happened to you? How did you become such a mess?"

Wincing in pain, I struggled to find a comfortable position. "Walking home. Wind. Hit by a car." Then darkness again.

Maamaan sat perched in a chair beside me, wringing her hands when I awoke.

"Oh, thank God!"

She handed me a white pill, assuring me it would reduce the pain." I struggled to sit up, enough to down the pill and again came blissful sleep.

Papa sent Maamaan home and woke me after he closed the shop. "Time to go home. Can you stand?"

I was surprised at how much better I felt, but, when I attempted to stand, a fierce pain took my breath away. Papa scrunched his eyebrows together and pushed his silver hair back away from his eyes to help him think. He turned, faced his many shelves of medicine searching for something specific, then came back to my side holding a syringe.

"Where exactly is the pain coming from?" I pointed to my left hip.

He gently pulled up my skirt to reveal an enormous, black bruise. He touched the area with his cold hands pushing and poking until my scream indicated he had found the exact spot. He disinfected my battered hip and injected me with a lightning bolt of fire.

I fell back into a light sleep, later awakening to Papa's voice.

"Zhila, try to stand now."

Reluctantly I got up and put a little weight on my leg. It was a miraculous improvement, almost as if the accident had not happened.

"Papa, you are a wizard. I feel so much better."

A big smile erupted on his handsome, tanned face and he extended a strong hand to steady me.

I will never know if the driver tried to alert me. I think not. My life was not even worth enough for them to stop and see if I was dead or alive. But a constant reminder of that day etched itself deep into my psyche to nag me for a lifetime.

6

THERE ARE TWO EDUCATIONAL SYSTEMS IN IRAN: private and public. In both systems, separate schools are set up for boys and girls, segregated for religious considerations and to reduce distraction. If families cannot afford to enroll their children in private school, they attend the second-rate public system. The private schools offer higher salaries, so of course attract the top teachers and produce better results. My sisters and I went to a private school for girls in our neighborhood — not a top-rated school, but it was adequate. Ziggy attended the Rouzbeh School, known for its rigorous curriculum and the best in our district for boys.

According to his teachers, Ziggy resented taking orders or direction from them and rarely completed his assignments. Consequently, my parents received a final warning from his school informing them that he was failing his subjects. If he did not begin to demonstrate dramatic improvement, he would be expelled. This had humiliating implications for our family since Ziggy would be forced to transfer to an inferior public school.

Papa sat my brother down at the kitchen table, shoved the warning letter at him, and shrieked, “It says here the only subject you excel at is English. Every other subject you are failing. What is wrong with you? How could you do this to me? You are an embarrassment to our family!” He ranted red-faced, spittle flying wildly, until he was depleted and then stormed out of the kitchen.

The Shirazi living room was sacred ground, never used for *living,* only for entertaining. The plush, semi-circular couch was always covered in plastic, removed only for guests. A beautiful Persian rug framed the furnishings coordinating the design of this hallowed room. So, when Maamaan took Ziggy by the hand and walked him into this intimidating space, banned from all child activity, and invited him to sit on the forbidden, plastic couch, he knew big trouble was brewing. With tears in his eyes, afraid of what was coming, he nervously took a seat. Maamaan gently took his hand.

Papa shouts when he is angry, deflecting your attention. Maamaan whispers, immediately pulling your attention directly toward her like a magician. Zandra and I hid in the shadows eavesdropping, but whispers are difficult to perceive which is where my expert lip-reading skills came in very handy.

Maamaan started off on a positive note. “I’m so proud of you. You are getting an ‘A’ in English.” Then she wagged her finger at him. “But you are failing everything else. You are our only son, Ziggy-joon. You will carry our name to your children, and they to theirs. Do you want people to think the Shirazis are trash? If you are expelled from Rouzbeh and forced to transfer to Toloo, we will be disgraced. I know you do not want to humiliate your family, right?”

Toloo High School was known for its delinquent boys who were continually in trouble with the police. Sometimes even the secret police, the SAVAK, were called in to help investigate, using threats to bully the boys into submission.

Ziggy ran his fingers through his perfect brown hair, “I will do better, I promise.”

"I am counting on your promise," Maamaan said, pointing to the door, "Now get off my couch."

Ziggy sprinted for the back door and disappeared out of sight. I followed him to the backyard and watched as he climbed to the top limb of our old apple tree, his favorite place to sulk. It was difficult for me to climb trees and, as I raised myself onto the lowest branch, that familiar pain from my accident shot down my leg. I grimaced, took a deep breath, and hoisted myself up to the next branch, eventually making my way, up and settling on a branch across from Ziggy.

"I can help you," I said.

"And how can you do that, Zhila?" he sneered.

"We can do our homework together and, if you don't understand something, I will help you."

Ziggy's face brightened, "You mean you will do my homework for me?"

"How does that help you? How would you learn to think for yourself? Do you want to grow up stupid and useless? If you get thrown out of Rouzbeh, what will you do?"

"Go to Toloo."

"What kind of life would Toloo offer you?"

Ziggy jutted his chin out defiantly, "I don't care."

I reached up and picked two apples, handing one to Ziggy and taking a bite of the other. Staring into his charming, sad face, I said, "Our days can be good, bad, or horrible. What kind of day did you have today?"

"Horrible!"

"If you are smart, and I believe you are, you can change horrible to good. Believe it or not, some days can be worse than today."

"I know you have had worse days," Ziggy said with a bit of shame for his whining.

"Yes, but those days taught me just how strong and resourceful I can be when I must. There is always a way to solve every problem, even when it seems impossible. If you are expelled, what future or opportunity will you have? Maybe you will get arrested by the SAVAK and thrown into a dungeon. We might never see you again. Every day at Toloo and for the rest of your life would be a bad day. At Rouzbeh, you have a chance to learn and earn the grades needed for university. Then you are the master of your life and can control your destiny. You can choose any profession you like, doing work you love, creating the life you want, not one that is forced on you. Then you will have more good days than horrible, because your family will be proud of you and support you."

Ziggy threw his apple core at a building across the alley, and said, "I do need some better days, let's go do our homework."

I descended the tree slowly behind him, stiff from sitting so precariously, and relieved to finally be on firm ground.

Ziggy did indeed manage to graduate from Rouzbeh, but not without some frustration and a great deal of hard work. His transformation was astounding to everyone, and he finished in the top of his class. But the best reward for his diligence was the deep pride he saw in our parents' faces when they looked at him or spoke of his accomplishments. He made the Shirazi family very, very proud.

7

I LOVE *NOWRUZ*, THE PERSIAN NEW YEAR. It always begins on the first day of spring — my favorite season. School vacation for thirteen glorious days of the *Nowruz* celebrations only intensified my delight.

Papa closed the pharmacy for the day and we packed the car for a picnic in Shahr Park — an elegant 64-acre park complex in central Tehran. As was our custom for this special day, Papa parked at the northern gate near the Tehran Peace Museum.

Historically, Persians have been peaceful, loving people, and this museum was a testament to those attributes and a strong correlation to our culture. It advocates for peace by exhibiting the destructive nature and consequences of war. The displays show the costly impact war has on health, environment, and economy when problems are solved with slaughter and death.

We walked past the front of the museum, marveling at the sculpture of a dove perched on a military helmet clearly pointing to the dichotomy of war. We looked out over fields of green, searching for an empty picnic table near the lake competing with a flock of people looking for their perfect spot to enjoy the *Nowruz* feast, too.

Ziggy and Papa each held an end of the large picnic basket, hurrying ahead of us to stake claim to a table. I pushed Zanna in her stroller, while Zandra and Maamaan held hands, stopping now and again to admire the purple tulips glistening in the sunlight.

"What do the tulips smell like?" I asked.

Zandra stuck her nose in the flower, giggled and looked back at me. "Imagine that: a flower with no fragrance."

It was a beautiful day with a few puffy clouds hovering in a magnificent blue sky. Paddleboats plodded by, creating ripples on the water, interrupting the mirrored reflections of hazelnut and pine trees. I took a deep breath of fresh, spring air, so happy that temperatures had finally warmed after the cold winter.

Maamaan converted the picnic table to a *Haftseen* table with a white tablecloth designating the New Year celebration. Zandra unpacked the picnic basket while Maamaan artfully arranged flowers in assorted jars and lit two ritual candles. She then placed the customary seven edible items of our nation's ancient Zoroastrian religion on the table to complete the traditional display.

Maamaan had worked meticulously to make the *Kuku* picnic, the first of the New Year, very special. Most unique among the seven ritual items she prepared was a decorative pot filled with everyone's favorite: *Sabze,* sprouted wheat gum, symbolizing birth and growth. She planted it in February so it would be ready for this celebration.

The remaining six items she prepared were *Samanu*, a sweet pudding, symbolizing affluence; *Senjed* olives, representing love; *Seer*, (garlic) for good health; *Seeb*, red apples expressing beauty; *Serkeh*, vinegar representing old age and patience, and the last of the symbols, *Sumac,* a fruit placed behind a lit candle conveying the color of sunrise.

While Maamaan set out our lunch, Zandra, Ziggy, and I tried to keep three-year old Zanna occupied, although she was more interested in pushing the stroller herself as opposed to being pushed. She leaped out to supervise her stroller as we walked along the path, until Maamaan signaled that lunch was ready. In joyful tribute Ziggy kicked his soccer ball high into the air and caught it as if celebrating a victory.

We all sat lazily on a bright yellow blanket, lips only moving to relish Maamaan's delicious spread. Ziggy smartly took advantage of the festive mood to ask Papa for permission to go skiing the following week with his friend Fayaad.

Maamaan shook her head a vigorous NO! But Papa ignored her.

"Your grades have improved a great deal. I am proud of you, so yes, you may go!"

As he finished his sentence, he exchanged looks with Maamaan, who, after a few thoughtful seconds, nodded in agreement. Ziggy threw himself into the air and did his traditional victory dance, punctuated by his famous backflips.

"Fayaad is so cute," Zandra sighed with a dreamy expression, "He has long dark hair and a dimpled chin. Has he ever asked about me, Ziggy?"

"Yes!" he grinned, "I told him you were a dork." Then he doubled over laughing at his teenage cleverness.

I offered to help Maamaan clean up after our meal while everyone else went for walks or to meet friends. Maamaan tapped me, and said, "I don't worry about Zandra; she is pretty and intelligent. She will find a good man when it is time."

"I have no doubt you are right," I said warily, not quite sure where this conversation was going.

"But you — I worry about you. Men tend to be egotistical. They want women to listen to them; hear what they are saying without having to repeat themselves. I am afraid men will run the other way once they realize you cannot hear."

I bristled, and looked at my mother coldly. "You think I will never find a good man because I am deaf."

Even though the park was noisy, I could still hear cheerful sounds floating through the air, but my happy mood was shattered at Maamaan's implication.

I glared at her as I folded the tablecloth. "A good man will accept me for who I am and if he does not, to hell with him!" I threw the folded tablecloth at the picnic table and stormed off.

I walked briskly to calm the rage welling up inside me. I came upon an alluring copse of trees and noticed a piece of shale sticking up from behind a clump of grass. This would be a nice addition to my rock collection. I began to regain my composure and sauntered to the edge of the lake watching a young couple in a paddleboat. Grey clouds began to fill the horizon, looking like a spring storm was forming, and I noticed the girl in the boat hold onto her shawl as the wind whipped up around her. I felt a quick twinge of pain, taking me back in time to my own wind whipped scarf incident. So often I am forced to relive that memory unexpectedly, jogged by the most mundane of reminders. Would I ever escape the trauma of that day?

I wandered back to our picnic area, fiddling with my piece of shale for comfort, and I began thinking about the beautiful clothing Aunt Sabra made for herself. Maybe I could learn to design my own glamorous clothing and look as stunning and stylish as she. Maybe then boys would be so taken with my appearance that my deafness would become an insignificant matter. I scolded myself for having such a shallow opinion of my worth, tying it only to my physical appearance. But it helped me discover this novel view of my deafness as being insignificant.

This was a revelation that eclipsed all else becoming my deepest desire. What a lovely realization to begin the New Year.

8

AUNT SABRA AND UNCLE IZZY DIVORCED and she had bought a house across the city in District Two on Hafezi Street. Her former gray and white, two-story house was much larger than this new one, but, as happens when a marriage dissolves, one does not need as much space.

This was the day Aunt Sabra promised to teach Parry and me how to sew. I was so excited that she had agreed to set aside this time and we would be taught and supervised by a master. Our first lesson to begin our initiation into the world of self-made apparel would be to design a dress for an upcoming school party.

As I stood on the expansive front porch, I could feel vibrations, like a herd of buffalo charging, to answer my knock. The door flew open and Cousin Parry threw her arms around me in a tight welcome hug, then cheek kisses.

"You made it, Cousin! I am so happy to see you. You are just in time for lunch."

"*Taftoon!* I can smell it. I am famished."

We joined Cousin Joe at the kitchen nook, where he perched hungrily like a lion cub waiting to be fed. Aunt Sabra placed a tray filled with neatly sliced vegetables and cheese on the table and then fresh from the oven, the aroma signaling that it was time to eat — the much anticipated Persian flat bread, *Taftoon.*

Since boys and girls in Iran attended separate schools, there were very few opportunities for them to socialize outside of family gatherings. Our school principal had established a yearly tradition to host a celebration at her home where her students could meet or get to know each other better. At the end of each school year, for students of the proper age, she organized a lavish party in a safe and supervised environment. After introductions to those they did not know, they would have the rest of the summer for opportunities to organize activities of their own.

Joe was a growing teenager with a voracious appetite and always seemed to be hungry. He quietly sat, gobbling his lunch, his square shoulders hunched while he shoveled in mouthfuls of feta-covered *Taftoon.* In between bites he asked, "Zhila, who is going to the party?"

"I know Ziggy and Zahra will be going, and Ziggy mentioned a few of his friends will be going, too."

We chattered on about who might be coming, and how wonderful her party was always rumored to be.

As we finished lunch, Aunt Sabra stopped Joe as he tried to disappear out the back door. "Not so fast, Joe."

"What?" he asked sharply.

"I want you to clean up the kitchen before leaving."

"That is women's work, Parry should do it."

Parry spun around on her heels ready to protest, but was abruptly cut off before she could utter a syllable. "You will clean the kitchen. Do we understand each other?" He nodded, knowing it was hopeless to argue with that expression and intense tone of voice, and began to clear away the lunch dishes.

We went upstairs to the small sewing room to get started with our lesson. It was a cozy, aesthetic space with a corner table supporting a sewing machine and a cutting table piled with rolls of fabric. On the wall above the sewing machine hung ten rows of spools filled with thread. Alongside the colorful spools hung an artistic, Farsi needlework displaying the text, *Create* and *Sew*.

Aunt Sabra put her arm around the adjustable mannequin standing proud in the center of the room and explained how we would use her for measuring and fitting our dresses. She pointed out the rolls of fabric lying on the cutting board from which to choose. Parry chose a roll of blue material for her dress and I a plaid Scottish tartan.

We spent the day learning the basics of how to create a garment, choosing and pinning a pattern, measuring and cutting fabric, and, of course, how to use the sewing machine to put it all together. There were many steps requiring me to look down and concentrate quite a lot, so lip-reading while chatting was not possible if I wanted to end up with a wearable piece of clothing.

After several hours of concentrated effort, Parry took a break, and Aunt Sabra quickly took advantage of the opportunity to have a private conversation, making me promise that the information was to be kept strictly between us.

"Uncle Izzy is a very rich man, as you may know, and thankfully your cousins will never have money worries, but I also want to make sure that you are given the same consideration.

"Your mother has shared with me that you are deaf, and I realize that will present serious challenges in your life that others would not face. I want to do what I can to ease that burden. I have instructed my sister, your Aunt Rebecca, that in the event of my passing, she is to turn the deed to this house over to you. You are free to do with it as you wish."

"Oh my God, you are not dying, are you?" Tears filled my eyes, distorting my vision as I embraced her.

She held me at arm's length, "No, I am perfectly healthy. I am just thinking ahead to your future when you are old like me. Now stop crying or Parry will suspect something."

"I do not know how to properly thank you, Aunt Sabra. This is such a generous gift and I am deeply grateful," I said, hugging her again.

Parry appeared in the doorway, "I leave for five minutes and return to a hug-fest."

I turned to my cousin with a smile. "I am just very grateful to Aunt Sabra for arranging this extraordinary day, I have learned so much."

That evening, as I sat in my room admiring my beautiful new dress, I envisioned myself a princess, slipping into a beautiful gown, searching for my Prince Charming.

9

GOLI AND I SOMETIMES would muster our courage and walk over to Ziggy's school with the excuse of meeting him when school let out. If we were lucky, some of his friends would tag along on the walk home.

With the party only a week away, we took a chance to meet him at school, this time with the goal of scoping out which of his friends might be planning to go to the party. Ziggy and Cousin Joe stood in front of the school's iron gate with a gorgeous, long-haired boy who fit Zandra's description of Ziggy's friend, Fayaad. His dimpled chin and glowing smile made my heart flutter.

I tapped my watch, signaling to Ziggy that we should be going, and his friends fell in behind him to leave.

Fayaad startled me by suddenly appearing at my side. "I am your brother's friend Fayaad, you are Zhila, right?"

I nodded, captivated by his full lips and a face that I could stare at all day.

Goli poked me in the ribs to remind me that she was also present.

"Oh, I am sorry, my manners are awful, this is my best friend, Goli."

"Nice to meet you, too. I heard that a teacher at your school is having a party. Is the invitation open for all students?"

"Actually, it is the school principal, Miss Askari, who is hosting it. She wants to create an opportunity for us to meet so that, if we want, we can continue to socialize during the summer. She arranges this party at her home every year when school dismisses. It is not open to everyone, but boys from your school have always been welcome."

Fayaad smiled and my heart beat a little faster as he asked, "Will you be going?"

"Oh yes," I looked at Goli. "We are looking forward to it."

As we rounded the corner, an immense, two-story house supported by large, marble pillars stood before us. I ran over to the rock wall base that supported the towering iron fence topped with sharp pinnacles. Grabbing hold of the fence, I dug my toes into a rock for a foothold and boosted myself up so I could see.

"It is beautiful! It has a wondrous yard with a playground and a stage with a dance floor."

I jumped down and, as I landed, I was instantly reprimanded not to do these things. I took a deep breath giving the pain a moment to diminish before turning to face the boys. Ziggy, Joe, and Fayaad took a turn on the wall, and gaped at the luxurious yard.

"Do you know who lives here?" Fayaad asked.

"This is the house where the party will be held, Miss Askari's home."

• • •

In the early afternoon of the party, I began primping — meticulously grooming my hair and face applying all manner of creams, a trace of cosmetics and, of course, the last touch: a dab of perfume. I slipped into my best undergarments, carefully selected the perfect shoes, and lastly put on my tartan dress. Transformation complete!

It was too early to leave for the party, so I nervously paced and waited, checking and rechecking the mirror for anything smudged or out of place.

The Askari mansion was even more breathtaking inside its metal gates. Goli, Joe, Ziggy, Zandra, and I ascended a flight of marble steps, delivering us to a wide portico with a heavy glass door that opened smoothly with a gentle push.

A tall, lean boy, about college age, greeted us in the foyer, extending his hand to Joe. He introduced himself as Jasper, the principal's son. Joe shook his hand and presented each of us by name so that we were properly acquainted. Zandra came to my side to quickly fill in what I had missed.

Jasper led us through their home, each room more impressive than the last. We wound our way through, finally exiting into what looked like a perfectly manicured park. I gasped as I looked across the palatial expanse. There was a swimming pool surrounded by a wrought-iron fence with balloons attached, bobbing in the breeze. A lounge area was to my left and children swinging and playing on the playground to my right.

A group of teen musicians, calling themselves The Muslim Brothers, were setting up their equipment and tuning their guitars and instruments in the rear of the yard. Surrounding a large dance floor stood a semicircle of cypress trees, forming a sheltered space beckoning couples to come and celebrate.

An ice sculpture of a dolphin graced a long table near the pool, filled with colorful bowls of fruits and vegetables, dipping sauces, assorted refreshments and drinks. We were starving, so first thing we descended on the food table, filling our plates. I found an empty, round table perfect for lip reading, and we feasted like barbarians.

The band started up and Ziggy immediately recognized his favorite Beatles song, "Help", so he grabbed a handful of chips, jumped to his feet, and headed for the stage. The music was very loud since the band had to compete with people splashing in the pool, teens celebrating, and toddlers happily screaming on the playground.

Goli and I had practiced swiveling our hips for days to learn the most recent American-style dancing. She had instructed me to pretend to be squashing a bug on the ground with my shoe, moving it back and forth to match the swivel of our hips.

To her delight, she announced, "Our efforts have been validated. Bless The Muslim Brothers they are playing our song." We ran to the crowded dance floor and *twisted* to Chubby Checker's hit, "The Twist", a popular American favorite. I prepared myself for the familiar attack of pain, hoping I could keep it masked behind a smiley façade. Fortunately, as the song ended, I only had a few twinges reminding me to take it slow.

I felt a tap on my shoulder and, as I turned, I found myself face-to-face with Fayaad. There was that smile again, framing those beautiful lips. I watched them say, "May I have this dance?" I nodded numbly as he took my hand to escort me to the dance floor.

My dreamy mood was temporarily interrupted by a sharp pang of guilt as I noticed the crestfallen expression on my sister's face. We distanced ourselves from Zandra and I told him, "My sister, Zandra is attracted to you, so, to keep peace in the family, after this dance you must dance with her twice before I will dance with you again."

Fayaad looked over my shoulder at Zandra, smiled, waved, and agreed to my terms.

Fayaad danced to the music with an assured confidence, and I followed him closely to keep from looking like a klutz. He guided me around the dance floor, masterfully avoiding collision with other couples. When the music stopped, he politely thanked me and made a beeline to the refreshment table.

Goli, Zandra, and I stood gossiping at the edge of the dance floor, and Goli blurted out a remark about how cute Fayaad was, not realizing that Zandra had a serious crush.

Zandra's anger had been building since she saw me dancing with Fayaad and, after Goli's comment, it came pouring out. Turning to me red-faced, she yelled, "You are such a traitor!"

"No, it is not what you think. You misunderstand, sister. Fayaad only wanted to dance with me so he could ask about you," I lied.

Zandra's eyes widened, "Really? What did he say?"

Over her shoulder, I saw Fayaad approaching, "Ask him yourself."

Fayaad tapped her on the shoulder and the two strolled off to the dance floor. I have never seen my sister beam as brightly as that night.

While they were enjoying their slow second dance, a chubby girl with short brown hair pointed in their direction and screamed out, *johod*! In Farsi, *johod* is an anti-Semitic racial slur. It is most often aimed at Jews to announce to anyone who may be listening: *Beware, they contaminate everything they touch.* Fayaad's face turned crimson, and he crudely pushed Zandra away, bolting off the dance floor, leaving my poor sister humiliated and in tears.

To Jasper's credit, he recruited a young woman who grasped the anti-Semite's fat wrist and briskly escorted her from the party.

As she was being led away, the girl turned and screamed to the crowd, "They are not Iranian! They are Jews! They are subversives that we allow to live here. Why are they allowed to be here at OUR party?"

Ziggy quickly filled me in on what had happened, and then gallantly ran to the dance floor to rescue our weeping sister.

Deafness sometimes has its benefits. I am protected from foul comments like these, but, tragically, my friends and family have related stories of their vile encounters with this sort of verbal bigotry. Once in my father's pharmacy, Ziggy overheard a nasty conversation between customers about how Jews were really Israelis disguised as Iranians who learned to speak Farsi.

Ignorance abounds. In truth, Jews settled in Persia twelve hundred years before the Arabs conquered the country and forced us to convert — before it was called Persia. And yet, we still are denounced as outsiders. It grieves us deeply to be treated by our countrymen as *johod.*

It was not surprising that no one came to express their regret or apology after the incident — not even the host. She likely chose silence to avoid offending her Muslim students. The only non-Jew to walk away with us was my dear friend, Goli. But the most disheartening revelation of all: Fayaad was nowhere to be found.

Since Principal Askari did not possess the kindness or good manners to soothe the insult of the humiliating outburst, the joyful mood of the evening was shattered. We retreated back down the marble steps to the comfort of home.

As we reached the bottom step, Zandra grabbed my hand and said, "Fayaad is a complete jerk!"

I nodded, and we both broke into spasms of laughter.

10

EVERY JANUARY, BETWEEN SCHOOL SEMESTERS, students are rewarded with a ten-day vacation. My 16th birthday fell during this break, and Ziggy invited me to join him and Fayaad for a day trip skiing in the Alborz Mountains, about a ninety-minute drive from Tehran. I agreed to go, although I was hesitant because I had not seen Fayaad since his disturbing behavior at the party six months earlier. He had some explaining to do.

Fayaad picked us up in the early morning hours as the sun was coming up. I had never skied before, so I borrowed a pair of skis from Aunt Sabra to be able to test out this new sport. Fayaad's Volkswagen bus was loaded with gear on top, so we added ours and jumped into the bus heading north to Darbvandsar, the town situated at the highest elevation in Iran.

Once out of the city, the roads turned to smooth asphalt, making for a much more comfortable ride. We passed expansive, green valleys with the snow-covered Alborz Mountains looming ahead of us. The radio belched out incomprehensible noise, so I reached over and turned it off.

"Hey! I was listening to that," complained Ziggy.

I put my finger to my lips to signal his silence.

I positioned myself so that I could see Fayaad's lips as best I could, sometimes using the rearview mirror for a better view, and got right to the point. "Why did you leave Zandra on the dance floor at the party like she was a pariah johod?"

Fayaad's face reddened with embarrassment as he made a clumsy effort to explain. "You are very direct! I do owe you an explanation, and I do apologize for being so rude, but I was so embarrassed and just wanted to get out of there. The fat girl who called me a *johod* lives in our district and has assigned herself the duty to denounce our family in public every time she sees any of us."

"Wait," I said, very confused, "You? I thought she was calling Zandra a *johod!*"

"Why did you think that? Are you Jewish, too?" he asked.

I nodded, and we looked at each other while the information sunk in, and then broke into hysterical laughter at how absurd the confusion had become.

"My father is Jewish and my mother is Muslim. Stupid people call us *johod* all the time. I hate dealing with it, so I bolted from the party."

"Well then, of course, apology accepted," I said, "I needed to resolve this before we arrived at the ski resort, otherwise it could have made for an awkward day."

We reached the foothills and the wind slammed hard against the bus as the road narrowed. The winding road was flanked on one side by a steep stone wall covered with packed, icy snow. Signs along the road cautioned, "Danger! Rockslide Area".

"This road seems very dangerous," I said, my voice shaky.

Fayaad shook his head. "It will be fine. The road has been plowed and it is only dangerous in the spring when the snow and ice melt. With the thaw, rocks tend to dislodge and fall, but this time of year has never been a problem." He eased my mind somewhat, but the occasional wind gusts hitting the bus terrified me.

Fayaad drove slowly, relieving more of my tension, and eventually the plowed road opened up to the parking entrance, but unfortunately there was no parking left. The lot faced the red brick ski lodge, its roof piled high with snow. Signs pointed the way to additional parking a kilometer away, so we kept driving.

It took us a while to hike from the parking lot back to the lodge, especially loaded down with our gear. I wished they had offered a shuttle, because I was exhausted and having back pain. I found a comfy chair inside the warm lodge and closed my eyes to nap for a minute and rest my back.

Ziggy poked me awake and with a big grin on his sweet face handed me a lift ticket announcing, "Happy Birthday, Zhila!"

"Ziggy!" Fayaad smiled, "You never mentioned it was Zhila's birthday. We must do something special today."

"Skiing is special, so let's go!"

As we left the lodge, a cold breeze slapped me, announcing, *Wake up! You are going skiing!*

Ziggy put on his boots, snapped in his skis, waved good bye, and glided away, preparing for a position on the next seat on the lift.

I expected Fayaad to follow him, but instead he pleasantly surprised me by staying behind. "You mentioned this was your first-time skiing. Would you like me to give you a lesson?"

I nodded vigorously, very relieved and impressed at his gentlemanly character. He instructed me how to buckle into my borrowed skis, and told me to jump up and down a few times to make sure I was correctly snapped in, so they were tight and would not come loose. He showed me what to do with the poles and how to walk with them. I had no doubt that I looked like a fat, waddling duck. The mental image made me laugh as Fayaad grinned back at me.

We slowly made our way toward the green circle marking the lift for the beginners run — the opposite direction from the intermediate slope that Ziggy chose.

As we got closer to the chairlift, Fayaad said, "Watch how everyone gets on."

I studied people as they stood watching over their shoulder for the next chair to swing in behind them, then plopping down on the bench as it scooped them up. It was a chair ballet and timing was crucial. Our turn came, I held my breath, and dropped into the seat as I had observed the others do.

Fayaad pulled the chair's restraining bar down into our laps.

"That was easier than it looked," I said, finally able to exhale.

His hand had brushed against my arm, sending a thrill through me as we settled in. I was surprised at my reaction, and felt a little self-conscious, so I looked away, pretending interest in the skiers on the chair behind us.

The ride up the mountain was breathtaking. Beneath us, skiers flew down the white packed run. The sun reflected with a blinding glare off the snow and I was glad I wore sunglasses. I was unnerved at how long the run seemed from the air; the slope down below looked frightening.

Fayaad watched me, reading my expression. "No worries. It is the shortest run and has a nice gradual slope. You will see when we get down there. For now, just enjoy the view."

As we got close to the top of the hill, he nudged me to watch how the others got off the lift. I studied them and copied their moves, clumsily pushing myself off the bench, then coasting away from the lift.

At the top of the run, he demonstrated how to stop and turn, and pointed to a girl to watch as she whizzed by zigzagging down the slope, her hair flying.

"Are you ready to try?" he asked.

"I guess I better be, I have to get down the hill somehow."

"Just take it slow and, if you begin to feel out of control, use the stopping method I showed you and you will be fine."

I took a deep breath, and followed the girl's path down the hill, making a slow, wide serpentine like a frightened turtle.

A crowd of skiers flew by, making me feel like an uncoordinated oaf. Fayaad stayed close by encouraging me with that mesmerizing smile.

"Those skiers had a first day on the mountain too, so pay no attention to them."

Ice stung my face like needles, but the sensation was exhilarating. As I reached the bottom of the run, there was Ziggy applauding my success.

"That was so much fun. I want to do it again!"

We did do it again and again, up and down that mountain, at least a dozen runs or more.

Ziggy and Fayaad kept me company part of the day on Zhila Mountain — their teasing reference to my beginner's hill — later escaping to the runs more suited to their skill. I stayed on my hill, improving with each run down the hill, and getting comfortable in my new-found amusement.

As the sun was beginning to set, Fayaad offered to treat us to a special dinner at the lodge to celebrate my birthday before leaving. His generosity made me blush, which only intensified when he flashed that bright smile.

During dinner, Fayaad said something to me that required an answer, but I was looking down at my plate and completely missed that he had spoken to me.

"Do you agree with that?" He repeated.

"Do I agree with what?"

An awkward silence dominated the table and I realized I was trapped. The time had come to make a decision: Do I start advocating for myself and stop pretending that I could hear? Or do I lie again and feel like a mumbling fool?

Both choices made my stomach turn over. Terrified, I began to tell my lifelong secret.

"This seems like a fitting time to tell you: I am deaf."

I paused, waiting for Fayaad's horror or pity or whatever reaction was to come, but he sat respectfully for me to continue the story.

"When I was three, I almost died from a serious infection called meningitis. It can result in blindness, deafness, or other disabilities. I lost almost all of my ability to hear, so I rely on lip-reading to know what people are saying to me. If I cannot see your lips, I will have no idea what you are saying or, as in this case, that you are talking to me."

Waiting for his impending condemnation, Fayaad said, "I will have to remember to look at you when I am speaking and, if I forget, please remind me." Then his mind started whirling with all the adjustments and ramifications this new information entailed. "What about the darkness? We will have to drive home with the cabin light on … I apologize, I am just thinking out loud of things to consider."

I nodded, not able to speak for the tight knot of tears stuck in my throat. I pressed my fingers to my lips embarrassed to let out my euphoric relief and savoring the absolute gratitude in my heart.

"I am curious," Fayaad said. "Is lip-reading hard to do?"

"I am not really sure how to answer that; it has always been my primary way of communicating. I do not really think about how I do it. I guess the best way to answer that is to demonstrate. I will turn off my voice and just mouth the words of a sentence and you see if you can understand what I am saying."

I mouthed: *Did you have a nice day?*

Fayaad guessed at several possibilities, and got them all wrong, realizing, while we all laughed together, that, yes indeed, it was an extremely difficult task.

"Very few people in our family know Zhila is deaf; that's how good she is. She inspires me every day." Ziggy said.

"The most difficult part of being deaf is the unkind way that people react. Disability is not accepted well in our culture. We are kept secret so that we do not shame our family. If discovered, we are pitied and then ignored. I would be a liability to my family if people knew. They would judge my parents as inferior. This is why no one knows. With that burden on me, I had to become an expert lip-reader; it was purely survival."

"I had no idea. I have never known anyone with a disability. I feel honored that you told me and will respect your privacy and protect your secret."

This was the most wonderful dinner I had ever had and would forever hold it in my heart as one of my sweetest memories. The freedom to be myself without the need to be constantly on guard in fear of being found out was the most liberating feeling I had ever known. I realized if I wanted to keep this kind of freedom in my life, I must learn how to make deafness understood and accepted more widely. That would first require putting away the shame to which I had so subtly agreed. I had a lot of work to do.

We bundled up, picked up our gear, and trudged through the Arctic wind back the long, cold kilometer to the VW.

Fayaad concentrated carefully as he drove the dark, icy road. Even with the cabin light switched on, conversation was kept to a minimum.

As he pulled up and parked the bus in front of our house, he looked at me and said, "I was hoping I could see you again."

"You mean a date?" I asked.

Fayaad's face flushed as he nodded.

"Yes, I would love that very much." For the second time that day a thrill of excitement surged though my body.

Ziggy and Fayaad flashed each other a reassuring look, smiling triumphantly as if they had just pulled off a grand coup.

11

FAYAAD AND I HAD BEEN SEEING EACH OTHER at least once a week since our trip to the mountains. We would meet and walk home from school together and talk about our lives. He tended to speak rapidly, but I had become accustomed to his cadence and lip movements, so it was getting easier to understand him without having to fill in with context. My mother's caution from years earlier about men's dislike of having to repeat themselves always lingered in my head, warning me to be careful not to ask for repeats too often.

"My family is celebrating the New Year, *Chahar Shanbeh Suri,* next Tuesday night and I would love for you to come to our family festival."

"That would be perfect! With *Nowruz* starting soon, I have no school next week, so my parents would allow it. I have never attended this festival, and know very little about it, so tell me whatever I need to know to avoid doing anything to embarrass you or myself in front of your family."

"I cannot imagine you embarrassing anyone, but I will give you some quick background. My mother's family traditions are rooted in Zoroastrianism, one of the oldest religions in existence. It was the dominant religion in Persia before Mohammed outlawed it. Their belief in One God is the same as in Judaism, but ethical beliefs also hold a high place of importance within the religion.

"The Persians experienced oppression under Arab rule, and most families were forced to convert to Islam. They retained their traditions and secretly celebrated, very similar to the history of the Jews.

"In Zoroastrian tradition, Wednesdays are believed to be unlucky days — especially the last Wednesday of the year. This celebration, also called the Festival of Fire, always begins on the last Tuesday night of the year — sort of like insurance to prevent the last of any Wednesday disasters. The rituals of the festival you must personally experience to understand, and it will be outside, so bring a sweater."

Fayaad's home had a very high wall protecting it and the front gate had a security system requiring one to press a button signaling the resident that someone had arrived. I pushed the obvious button and waited, pushed again, and waited and waited …

Contemplating what I would do next, the gate finally opened and Fayaad popped out to show me in.

"I am sorry. We buzzed you in and I forgot that you would not hear the buzz. It seems there are still many things I need to remember about being deaf."

I was annoyed at him for forgetting, and even more irritated with myself for feeling I had to hide it from my boyfriend and apologize for being an inconvenience. *Would I ever meet someone who truly understood what it is like to be deaf?*

I followed him through his beautiful home, noticing the Persian rugs covering select areas of white, marble floors adorned with beautiful antiques. A number of large windows allowed the remaining glow of twilight to scatter on the white marble floor.

The backyard served as the setting for the event, with a lovely spread of specialty foods, vases of colorful flowers, and helium-filled balloons. A separate decorative table held curious animal and human figurines made of clay.

I pointed to the table and whispered to Fayaad, "What are the clay figures?"

"This is a holiday with a lot of symbolism. Those figures are to honor the memories of our departed loved ones, including our pets." He picked up the model of a horse explaining it represented the horse his mother had when she was a girl.

I was suddenly distracted when, over Fayaad's shoulder, I saw a group of men carrying logs from a shed and interrupted him. "What are those men doing?"

"Remember when I told you this was known as the Festival of Fire? Those are the logs for the fires."

We positioned two chairs near a light so we could face each other as he resumed his explanation of the figurines.

"It was once believed that the living were visited by the spirits of their ancestors on the last day of the year …" Suddenly, our heads snapped toward the back door as five very noisy children burst into the yard wrapped in shrouds, beating pots with wooden spoons. "The children are reenacting the visits of our family ghosts." He looked directly at me and tried shouting above the noise, "They bang with the *Qashog-Zani* to beat out the last unlucky Wednesday of the year in the hope that it will pass without misfortune. Later tonight, they will knock on doors in the neighborhood asking for treats to be rewarded for a job well done."

Darkness descended and, without warning, the yard burst into flames. Fayaad's father and uncles stood next to the mounds of logs they had piled earlier and simultaneously set them ablaze, lighting up the yard.

When my heart stopped racing, I said a little prayer, thanking God for the additional light to help me lip read more easily.

"What is the purpose of the fires?"

"Bonfires are an old tradition. They are built to burn until Wednesday morning to promote happiness in the hopes that illness, worry, and pain will be devoured by the flames. It is all very symbolic for good health and the coming spring. Fire and light are supposed to help prevent anything bad from happening on the last unlucky Wednesday. Everyone is lining up to take a turn jumping over a fire as a purification ritual so that they can start the New Year cleansed."

Fayaad grabbed my arm and said, "This will be fun."

We came to a stop in front of one of the smaller bonfires made for the children, built so that the blaze did not climb too high and they could safely jump over the burning embers. Fayaad pointed to a young girl who jumped really high and yelled something indiscernible.

He instructed me, "When you jump the fire scream, *Sorkhi-ye to az man. Zardi-ye man as-b.*"

I loved the idea of having my back pain eliminated, but as the line grew shorter, my courage began to dwindle. As I faced the fire, my mind and legs lost touch with each other and refused to cooperate. I was concerned that jumping would aggravate my back, so decided to watch for a little longer and wait for the fire to burn down a bit.

I moved back into line when it appeared that I could safely jump and took my turn shouting the phrase Fayaad had taught me to say, *Give me your beautiful red color; take away my pale face,* making sure to jump high enough to avoid scorching my backside. We jumped and shouted several times for the healthy color to return to our faces and then headed for some well-deserved nourishment.

"Zhila, do you have any wishes?" Fayaad asked.

"Yes, of course. But right now, I wish to eat. I am starved."

He laughed and I admired the way it lit up his face.

"No, I mean a wish for something you dream about."

I nodded and started to speak, but he cut me off, putting his finger to his lips.

"Shhhh, do not tell me."

He handed me a bowl of Persian noodle soup and suggested I try one of the pastries filled with dried nuts and fruit.

"This is really good," I said talking with a mouth full.

"I am glad you like it. Now close your eyes and make a wish. It is believed that wishes will come true on the eve of *Chahar Shanbeh Suri*."

I wished to never be bothered by pain again, and we polished off the rest of the luscious wishing food.

Suddenly, spotlights went on all over the backyard.

I squealed. "That was one of my wishes too. I love this! Now what happens?"

Fayaad leaned forward as if he were about to kiss me, but instead grabbed my hand and said, "Come, let's see if your real wish will be granted."

He guided me to a secluded area, close to a group of men who sat conversing and smoking.

"Those men over there," he pointed, "Can you see their lips?"

I moved aside a branch that camouflaged our hiding place and peeked through, instinctively searching for a face without a moustache for an unobstructed view.

"Your uncle said something about having good business this year. That man next to him is saying something about good investments and that other guy looked up to the stars as if to say, *Thank you*."

I released the branch and stared at Fayaad, who had also been eavesdropping on the conversation.

"This is very good news," he said.

"For them, maybe, but why would that be good for us?"

He smiled. "The ancients believed that a wish would come true if a passerby were to overhear a positive conversation."

I got very excited that my wish would come true and gently wrapped my arms around Fayaad's neck and kissed him.

We drew apart and gazed tenderly into each other's eyes.

"The ancients were right! You just made my wish come true," he said slowly and took me into his arms for a long, slow kiss.

12

SIX MONTHS AFTER ARRIVING AT SHIRAZ UNIVERSITY, I received a letter from Goli: she wanted to visit during her midterm break. Since my roommate would be going home to Tabriz, I arranged for her to stay with me to avoid hotel costs. I had missed her terribly and was so excited she was coming.

Shiraz is a large enough city to support an international airport serving the Fars province and the entire southern region of the country. Late on Saturday afternoon, I hurried to the Iran Air terminal to meet her.

Goli deplaned the Boeing 707 looking like a fashion model, statuesque and curvy, sporting a stylish white blouse and jeans. She held a scarf close to her head to prevent the wind from pulling it away and waved at me from the back of the crowd. She pushed her way through the throng and we grabbed each other in an overdue embrace, kissed each cheek, and then hugged again. Gently pushing me to arm's length, she squealed, "It is so good to see you, Zhila!"

I grabbed her hands and we jumped up and down with excitement. "I cannot believe you are here standing in front of me!"

She looked at me and said, "You got glasses."

"Yes, I have become a bit nearsighted."

We collected her luggage from the carousel and then hopped on the bus to the university. Gossiping nonstop, we magically found ourselves on the steps of the dorm forty-five minutes later as if we had passed through a time warp.

I unlocked the door, stepped aside and announced, "Ta, Da! You may now enter my palace."

Luckily, I was able to find time to tidy the room before leaving for the airport, especially since it had not been cleaned since moving in. The tiny room was able to accommodate very limited furnishings: my bed, flush against the wall, came with a chest of drawers; a desk; and bookcase next to the bed. The opposite side of the room mirrored mine with my roommate Mana's furniture.

On the wall next to my bed hung my prized, *Gem of Peace* — a plaque Goli had given me for graduation. Within its red ceramic, raised edge was the Hebrew word *Shalom* intertwined around a peace symbol, made of gemstones, for my interest in geology.

Goli's sparkling brown eyes scanned the room as she nodded her approval. She went to the window and marveled at the palm trees and emerald-green lawn, lined with rows of bushes leading to the academic buildings.

"There were a few centimeters of snow on the ground when I left Tehran this morning. Imagine that! Just get on a plane and, *voila!*, I land in paradise."

Mana's wall boasted a black-bordered psychedelic poster of Jimi Hendrix with blue hair, holding an orange guitar.

"What is Mana like?" Goli asked as she studied the poster.

A tacit scowl appeared on my face, revealing my feelings.

"Roommate from Hell, huh?"

I laughed as I leaned on my pillow and hugged the doll my youngest sister had given me as a going-away gift. "I will just say she is not a nice person."

Goli sat down on the chair near my desk. "What seems to be the problem?"

"About a month ago, I returned to the dorm unexpectedly to get my geography book and I caught her leaving with my sewing machine tucked under her arm."

Goli's eyes widened. "What?!"

"She casually said she was borrowing it to fix a friend's outfit. What a lie! I grabbed it from her and told her she could use it here, but she must ask me first."

"Good for you!" Goli applauded. "Nice to see you are still standing up for yourself. What do you think she really wanted with it?"

"To sell it."

Goli's mouth dropped, "No!"

"Yes! Sometimes late at night, when she thinks I am sleeping, I see her inhaling white powder. Some of my clothes have gone missing and I suspect she is stealing things to sell for drug money."

"Did you report her?"

"No, but I threatened to. I confronted her last week. I looked directly at her and told her that if any more of my things disappear, I will report her to the dean. I decided to leverage it for your visit, telling her that you were coming and forthrightly said, 'My friend will be sleeping in your bed.'"

"What did she say?"

"Nothing; she just nodded. I guess under the circumstances, she assumed she had no choice but to agree."

Goli and I chatted well into the night, catching up with our lives. I had to get up in the morning to study before we could go off on our adventures, and she was exhausted from her long trip, so we climbed into bed and promptly fell asleep.

I awoke early to finish my geology assignment. I especially struggled in this class trying to understand my professor; my anemic class notes demonstrated my deficit. I sat at the front of the room staring intently at his lips when he spoke. Unfortunately, he had a tendency to turn around and face the board, writing while he spoke. Any hope of following him vanished, leaving a cavernous gap in my understanding. To compensate, I carefully read and re-read my textbooks, while taking copious notes.

A tap on my shoulder startled me.

"Sorry, I did not mean to frighten you," Goli said.

"No worry. Next time just flick the lights; that will get my attention. Did you sleep well?"

"Yes! Very fitting for paradise. What is the plan for today?"

I looked out the window. "The sky is clear with a few puffy clouds — seems like a perfect day to visit Vakil Bazaar."

Goli applauded and plopped down on my unmade bed. "That place is on my *must-see* list."

"What else is on that list of yours?"

"l would love to see Eram Garden and the Iran Perepolis," she answered.

"Two great places we can visit later in the week," I said.

We grabbed breakfast at a little café just off campus, and then boarded a bus to downtown Shiraz. Vakil Bazaar was located in the historical center of Shiraz, known for its huge, park-like courtyard. Goli gaped as we wandered through the bazaar's cavern-like hallways with brick walls and twenty-four foot-ceilings. Vendors piled rugs, decorative platters, and all manner of merchandise in every nook and niche on the tile floors. Every kind of nut, grain, and spice you could want were available at various shops. Despite the obvious distractions, today, I was focused on finding some new fabric.

Papa made sure I always had a generous allowance to cover my expenses, but thanks to Aunt Sabra's graduation gift, I saved on clothing. To reward my hard work, she proudly presented me with a brand-new, gleaming Singer sewing machine ordered from America.

It was a quiet day with little pedestrian traffic as we moved along the aisles of the bazaar. Some merchants bargained their wares, while others sat back smoking their hookahs, chatting with each other.

While resting against the wall of one shop, I spied a bolt of black fabric. *That would make a perfect dress for school,* I thought to myself. "How many meters of that fabric do you think I would need to make a dress?" I asked the seller, knowing the answer, but I wanted to see how honest she would be.

She eyed me for a quick second and said, "About six."

They usually overestimate, but she was close, and I decided I could use any extra to make scarves for Mamaam and my sisters. I nodded my consent for her to cut the material.

As she wrapped up my purchase, I looked around for Goli, but she was nowhere in sight. I began to panic, frantically searching one room after another, but could not find her anywhere. As I turned a corner, a noisy crowd in the courtyard got my attention, shouting and holding placards that read, *The Shah is a U.S. Puppet* and *Death to the Shah.* Even I could hear them shouting.

Across from the unruly throng stood a smaller, older group carrying Iranian flags and signs supporting the Shah. There in the middle stood Goli, shouting back at the opposition.

Relieved that I had found her, I leaned against a citrus tree across from where she stood, holding my package and waving. As soon as she saw me, she broke away and raced to my side. Breathless, she said, "Come, come, help me yell back at those fools."

"I did not know you were so political," I teased.

"They will destroy this country if they have their way. Come."

"No, I would rather not be involved, I will wait for you."

I wandered to a nearby bench to watch the demonstration, bringing back memories of the White Revolution, six years earlier. The Shah had begun implementing programs to modernize transportation, improve literacy, health, and conditions for women. There were those who opposed him, believing his reforms would disrupt the traditional system and weaken their authority.

The clamor of voices brought me back to the present as a contingent of the Imperial Guard, rifles drawn, marched into the courtyard. Goli scurried to my side and nervously said, "We must go!"

We lunched at the Sharzeh Restaurant next to Vakil Mosque and, as we ate our kabobs, Goli commented on my outfit. "Your skirt and blouse are so cute. Did you make them?"

"Yes, I am so glad you like them."

Goli took a sip of her tea. "You are so talented with that sewing machine."

"Thank you." I grinned and then laughed.

"What is so funny?" Goli asked, nibbling on a French fry.

"You made me think of an incident that happened at school when I was having lunch in the cafeteria. I was wearing this same outfit. Anyway, I noticed several girls looking in my direction, pointing at me."

"What did they want?"

"I thought maybe they liked my outfit. I can read lips pretty well and their comments were definitely not about my outfit. One of the girls said, 'I hear she's a Jew,' another said, 'I hear they are all rich.' Then a third asked, 'How do they make their money?' And then …"

Goli raised an eyebrow in anticipation. "What?" she demanded.

'I hear she sells drugs.'

Goli burst into laughter, apologetically covering her mouth as she laughed. We both giggled loudly as people near our table looked at us quizzically.

We spent the rest of the week visiting the places on Goli's "*must see*" list, but, as often happens with vacations, time slips away before you are ready.

We said a very tearful goodbye at the airport terminal and then, sadly, her sparkly brightness vanished, leaving me feeling hollow and alone, like part of me was missing. I missed her terribly before the plane even took off.

13

MR. NURI, A PERSIAN CARPET DEALER, lived next door to my parents while I was growing up. He had always appeared to be well off, but when I returned home for *Nowruz* during freshman year, his once beautiful home was now shabby and in serious disrepair. His exquisite yard was overrun with weeds, and the paint on his green and white residence was peeling away like skin falling from a rotting apple. I could not imagine what had happened to him, but Maamaan told me he had been drinking heavily.

On my third afternoon home, while sitting in the kitchen chatting with my mother over a cup of tea, Maamaan jumped as if something had scared her.

"What's wrong?" I asked.

"Mr. Nuri is having another of his outbursts."

I pressed my glasses up to the bridge of my nose and scrambled to the kitchen window, wondering what made my mother so nervous. Mr. Nuri was brandishing a large pair of shears at his seven-year old daughter, who was the same age as my sister, Zanna. She had gorgeous brown hair that could cause some adult men to take pleasure in fantasy.

I watched as Mr. Nuri drunkenly called for his daughter, who had scampered off to hide. "Julie, Juuulie … come out, come to papa."

The large window of his living room revealed a rotund and unkempt body; he had become appallingly obese in just a year. He slugged around, wielding the scissors like a weapon, and I could imagine how frightened Julie must have been, cowering somewhere, smartly hidden from his clutches.

"We are supposed to feel protected by our fathers!" I said in a rage.

I saw a small figure run out the side exit, with Mr. Nuri in sloppy pursuit. He reached out and managed to out maneuver the small child, grabbing one of her long braids.

I slammed the screen door behind me, and yelled to Maamaan to call the police.

I rushed to the Nuri home demanding to know, "What are you doing to that child?"

I summoned what I thought would be a loud voice that did startle Mr. Nuri, but the surprise on his face quickly turned ugly.

"Get off my property!" he shrieked. "Or I will cut off your hair too."

Julie escaped from her father's grasp and slunk away, appearing by my side and then moving to hide behind me.

"Where is Julie's mother? Does she know what you are doing to her daughter?"

"This is not your business!" he slurred. He swayed, with scissors flailing in the air pretending to cut my hair. "Those black tresses of yours would bring a good price!"

His perverted plan to sell his sweet daughter's hair to buy drink both saddened and disgusted me. I was witnessing alcohol transform an ordinarily loving father into a mean, pathetic bully.

It was baffling to imagine what demons must be torturing him to bring him so low as this.

I grabbed Julie's hand and slowly backed away. Just as we were about to elude disaster, we collided with a burly policeman coming up the walk. His appearance helped alleviate the violent pounding in my chest.

"I am Officer Sediqi," he said with an irritated glare. "What may I do for you?"

While I quickly explained the situation, Officer Sediqi took off his cap and stroked his bald head. "This is Mr. Nuri's home. He is allowed do as he wishes. You are interfering with matters of his home."

"Did not the Prophet of Allah tell us that man is the guardian of his family and every guardian has responsibilities towards those under his guardianship?" I asked.

"Yes," the officer reluctantly agreed, countering with his own lesson. "But the Qur'an states, *Men are the maintainers of women.*"

"This is true," I challenged. "But if a man wants to conquer the heart of his woman, would he do it with drink or with affection?"

With scissors clawed in one hand, betraying his scheme, Mr. Nuri stood wobbling, eyes aflame, incapable of concealing his stupor.

I pointed at Nuri. "He is drunk and trying to harm his daughter. I am here to prevent that."

The officer stared at Mr. Nuri. "Are you planning to harm this child?" He asked pointing to Julie.

Trying to muster a calm attitude and appear sober, he mumbled, "I just want to cut her hair."

Incapable of any empathy for this bloated drunkard, I shook my head in disgust, and said to Officer Sediqi, "Did not Prophet Muhammad say this about his daughter: *Fatima is part of me. Whatever pleases her pleases me and whatever angers her angers me.*"

The police officer nodded while trying to reason with Mr. Nuri.

"A father's role in his daughter's life is of great importance. I have a young girl of my own who I cherish. What purpose is served by scaring her this way?" He looked down at Julie who was shaking, then he raised his voice. "Look at her, she's trembling! This drunken behavior just confirms why alcohol is forbidden and illegal."

Realizing that I had bested Officer Sediqi in our ethical contest, I said, "I will take Julie with me until Mr. Nuri's wife comes home."

"Thank you for protecting the child," said Officer Sediqi, easing the tension.

From the safety of our home, I watched as the officer handcuffed Mr. Nuri and led him away. For his first offense, he would probably spend the night in jail and pay a fine, hopefully it would ward off any repeat episode.

"What is wrong with that man!" Maamaan said, "If you had not stopped him, he might have killed that child. Zhila, you made me very proud today."

I felt a tremendous confidence swell in my heart from my mother's praise and hugged her with genuine gratitude.

The day before I was to return to Shiraz, I had prepared sweets specifically to entice Ziggy to the table for a conversation. As I warmed the pastries, the mouthwatering aroma drifted through the house, pulling Ziggy into the kitchen.

I placed fresh baked baklava on a plate in front of him and his meaty hand grabbed for one asking, "How is Fayaad?

"Have you not spoken to him?"

Ziggy shook his head, took a bite, and sipped his tea. "He is too busy studying all the time."

I nodded knowingly. "That is what college is like. This is your last year of high school, have you given thought to your plans for next year?"

I let him contemplate the question as I swirled a teaspoon of honey into my tea.

"Zhila, how are your grades at Shiraz?" he finally asked evading my question.

I smiled, "All A's and B's, except math — never my strong subject."

"And Fayaad?"

"He says he has a 4.0 average."

Ziggy laughed, "He always gets straight A's. If he ever got anything less, I think he would become a nomad and wander the desert alone in shame."

I nodded. "I ask you again: Do you have any plans?"

In a seemingly non-sequitur response, he said, "Zhila, I am intimidated by you. I don't know how you sit through classes, missing probably half of what is said, and yet you manage to maintain high grades. I would be ashamed if I could not excel."

"Are you considering college?" I asked.

He reached into his back pocket and retrieved an envelope, holding it out to me and said, "This came in the afternoon mail."

I snatched the envelope from him, and stared at the embossed *University of Tehran* return address. I opened it and quickly unfolded the letter reading aloud:

It is with great satisfaction to inform you of your acceptance to the University of Tehran for next year. Congratulations.

"Oh my God! Ziggy!" His dazzling smile filled his handsome face. "I am so proud of you!"

• • •

Nowruz was over and I was adjusting to my school routine: up early, rush to class for that coveted front row seat, and pray for a good day. A few cruel classmates would occasionally mock me, their sheltered ignorance on parade, whispering while pointing and jeering, "She is the one who gazes dreamily at Dr. Abajami like he is a hot rock star."

My Chemistry professor, Dr. Abajami was no more enlightened than my callous classmates. I saw him one day on my way to chemistry lab. He was smoking his pipe, trying to appear very academic, while talking to a colleague. I waved hello, and he pointed to me, leering, as if I were his most recent conquest, displaying the conduct of a Neanderthal brute. "That is the student who is hot for me," I watched him say to his colleague.

I smiled sweetly and, just to amuse myself, wiggled my index finger seductively. He preened like a peacock, sucked in his fat gut, and strutted over at my behest expecting a sweet reward. We stood at the open door of the Chemistry Department — the perfect place to set his colleagues straight.

I slyly announced, in what I hoped was an emphatic voice, "Dr. Abajami, I am deaf, that means I cannot hear. I sit in the front row of your class to afford me the logistics to read your lips. I want to completely disabuse you of the idea that I am attracted to you in any way. My parents raised me well, so I assure you that I am not so foolish as to fall into that sort of unseemly trap. I simply want to earn my degree as best I can, with as few distractions as possible. Do we understand each other?"

That day, I learned the depths of vicious aberrations to which mankind can sink, but I also learned that one's self-respect can only be managed by oneself, so my remaining years at Shiraz thankfully passed with fewer cruelties and I graduated with honors.

14

A FEW MONTHS BEFORE GRADUATION, recruiters from all over Iran showed up at Shiraz University in search of graduates to fill positions at their companies. I made a beeline for Geo Tehran, the most reputable geology firm in Iran, with offices throughout the country. The recruiter was very kind, attentively explaining the procedure I needed to follow to be considered.

I sat at my desk carefully poring over the application form the recruiter had given me. I filled it out and attached a thoughtful treatise outlining my desire to join their firm, just as the recruiter had instructed. In mid-July I received a letter with a Geo Tehran return address. I opened it quickly, my heart pounding:

> *Congratulations Miss Shirazi,*
>
> *We are happy to welcome you to our team at Geo Tehran in the position of heavy mineral specialist. We will be assigning you to our team of experts who analyze*

lead, coal, iron, and uranium samples from different mining fields throughout Iran.

We feel certain that you will apply your inquisitive nature to provide new insights into these research studies and will be an asset to our company. We will expect your arrival on September 1, 1972 at our Tehran office."

Screams of joy brought, Ziggy, Zanna, and Zandra running from all directions.

"What is wrong!" Zanna cried.

Zandra rushed into the room and came to a halt before me, her face pale. "This better be good news," she said, "My heart almost stopped."

Ziggy tapped his foot impatiently, "Nu?"

"I got the job! Geo Tehran has hired me as a heavy mineral specialist. I start in September!" I jumped up and down waving the letter in my siblings' faces.

"You never cease to amaze me," my brother said with a look of admiration, mixed with a bit of envy. Shaking his head, he turned and strode back to his boy-cave.

Zanna, now ten, grabbed my hands and we danced around the kitchen table, her long braids bouncing in the air.

During dinner, I shared my wonderful news with Maamaan and Papa. They finished reading my letter and looked at each other with deep pride.

Papa winked slyly at my mother and she nodded. In his characteristically charming way, Papa said, "It is time to celebrate your glorious achievements. Zhila, what are your feelings about Europe?"

My hands flew to my mouth in shocked delight. "What?!"

"You leave next week for London, then France, and finally the *pièce de résistance*, Eritz Yisroel!"

I threw my arms around my parents and squeezed them. "Everyone is going?"

"Unfortunately, I must look after the pharmacy, and your sisters will be equally rewarded after they graduate college," Papa said, "But of course Maamaan will go and Ziggy will go in my place."

Ziggy, jumped to his feet with a huge grin and punched the air. "YES!"

A week later, Papa, Zanna, and Zandra accompanied us to the Mehrabad Airport to see us off on the TWA flight to London. I had never been outside Iran, and now here I was sitting on a glistening plane to London. I could hardly sit still.

Papa had made arrangements for us to meet his friend, Mr. Moshe Baum, when we landed. He was to be our tour guide and chaperone while in London.

Ten hours later, we touched down at Heathrow Airport, relieved to be on the ground again and anxious to start our adventure. A short, bald man with a brown beard, wearing a yarmulke, stood at the gate with a sign in Farsi indicating he was there to greet the "Shirazi Family." I found it interesting that once I saw his skullcap, there was recognition of immediate comfort in the kinship of another Jew. I had never experienced that in quite the same way.

He loaded us into his nondescript Volkswagen van and took off for the Leonard Hotel. I was actually in England. Everything looked so different than anything I was accustomed to.

"Mr. Baum?" I said, watching his lips in the rearview mirror.

"Call me Moshe," he said in a loud clear voice.

I liked him immediately. "Okay, Moshe, is the hotel in a good location for sightseeing?"

"The best! It is close to the Marble Arch."

"What is that?" Ziggy asked.

Moshe turned a corner, honking and waving at a passing car, and answered, "It is the famous entrance to Buckingham Palace."

Maamaan became uncharacteristically excited. "We will be staying near Buckingham Palace? I would love to visit the Queen's home first thing tomorrow."

Moshe smiled, "Alright then, that is the first place I will take you in the morning."

As the bellhop opened the door to our room, I gawked at the spacious two-bedroom suite. We were electrified, running around inspecting the rooms. Each bedroom had its own bathroom, the kitchen was not only fully equipped, but had a washing machine and dryer.

The evening light streaked through the windows in the bedroom that Maamaan and I would share. We had a lovely view of the street below from our sitting room.

"This will be a lovely oasis for the next three days," I told Maamaan.

True to his word, Moshe arrived early the next morning after breakfast to escort us to Buckingham Palace. "The Palace is a little over two kilometers from here, would you prefer to take the shuttle or walk?"

Unanimously, we agreed to walk so that we could better see the city. Unsure whether to wander slowly along the street to see everything we could, or to hurry to the palace, we struck a nice pace, allowing a glimpse of the U.S. Embassy, the Playboy Club, and the distinguished Wellington Arch — an impressive aggregate of very disparate places.

We walked along a wide pathway in Green Park, watching people in their beach chairs scattered across the lawn enjoying a rare sunny day in London. A flowered path meandered across the vast lawn and, through a wooded area, opening up to the eminent Buckingham Palace where a tour guide awaited us.

Even though Ziggy could speak English very well, Moshe had kindly arranged for a Farsi interpreter to accompany us so Ziggy could enjoy the tour and would not have to translate for us. As we approached, our guide, Amanda, and her interpreter moved forward to greet us. Amanda, a lovely young woman with a pale complexion, greeted us, offering her hand. She was so friendly and was so well-prepared, calling us by name and motioning with an elegantly outstretched arm for us to enter through the set of massive royal doors.

"There are long lines of people outside. How do we deserve such celebrity treatment?" I whispered to Moshe.

Moshe smiled. "Prince Philip, Queen Elizabeth's consort, is a personal friend of mine from our days in the war together. Philip told me long ago that any time my family or friends wished to visit London to let him know and he would ensure they received regal treatment."

"Buckingham Palace is the seat of the British monarchy and headquarters of the royal affairs of state," Amanda paused and our interpreter repeated her statement in perfect Farsi. "Its prominent art and architecture create a courtly statement exhibiting Britain's position in the world."

She opened the door to reveal a palatial ballroom. "This is the Throne Room." Amanda gracefully gestured toward duplicate pink elaborate chairs situated on a platform backed by plush red drapes as she quizzed us. "How many times do you think Her Royal Highness has availed herself of that throne to receive dignitaries such as your Shah?"

Ziggy blurted out his guess adding a fake British accent, "Two-hundred and twenty-five." His comedy made my mother laugh out loud which was unusual for her.

"Actually, this room is purely symbolic. Queen Elizabeth sat on that throne only once for her coronation in 1953. Good guess, Ziggy, and a pretty good accent."

Amanda guided us through the lavishly furnished palace, taking time to enlighten us with historical facts and interesting information about the royal family, and pointing out artwork by some of the world's greats.

Maamaan pointed to a Sevres goblet sitting on a silver tray. "That would make an elegant wine cup for Friday Shabbat," she said longingly.

Amanda laughed. "Yes, indeed. Unfortunately, your grandchildren would still be paying for it long after you are gone."

By the time the palace tour ended, we were famished, and grabbed a bite before taking the Underground to the famous 10 Downing Street. Still on our agenda for the day were several museums that we wanted to see, but the day was rapidly slipping away, and I began to think our plans were a bit overzealous.

Maamaan was exhausted, and the sights were becoming a blur, so we returned to the hotel. Ziggy and I were itching to check out London's nightlife, so we pulled up chairs to plan our adventure. Maamaan kicked off her shoes and fell into the plush comfort of the sofa in our suite, unable to keep her eyes open, she drifted off for a delicious nap.

Waking her gently, Ziggy quietly told Maamaan, "We are on our way to Piccadilly Circus to see what the London nightlife is like. We may be out for a couple of hours."

Maamaan yawned and then smiled groggily. "Ziggy-joon, what is Piccadilly Circus?"

"A circus, of course," he said, "with a lot of excitement, animals, and freak shows."

"Well, I am not sure how many animals or freaks you will find in a traffic circle," Maamaan teased.

"Huh?" he said, completely bewildered.

I intervened to save Ziggy from embarrassing himself further. "Do not worry, Maamaan, we will find our way around, I promise."

"But you have never travelled alone before, and you have no experience. It is dark out. What if you get lost, or worse, robbed?"

"Yes, Maamaan, but Ziggy speaks excellent English, so we will be fine, and we promise not talk to strangers," I teased. "Had you not become a wise mother before you were even twenty?"

"I know, I know, go, but promise me you will be careful, and do not be long, I will not be able to sleep until I see your faces again."

We changed into our jeans, and made a quick exit before Maamaan had a chance to change her mind. We caught a bus to

Piccadilly Circus, just to make sure Maamaan was serious about that traffic circle. We treated ourselves to a traditional dinner at a local pub: shepherd's pie, fish and chips, washed down, of course, with a pint of ale. The locals were friendly, the music loud, and the atmosphere thoroughly British — we loved it.

As we left the pub, it was raining, but a bicyclist pedaling a rickshaw coincidentally appeared in the downpour preventing us from getting soaked. We climbed into the leather-upholstered cab and its Indian driver asked, "Where to, mate?"

Ziggy handed the driver the address of the Leonard Hotel on Seymour Street and the driver pedaled straightaway through the slick streets, getting drenched as we sat protected under the cab.

He stopped in front of the hotel and said, "That will be ninety pounds."

"Ninety pounds!" Ziggy exclaimed. "You must be joking! Are you charging extra for the rain?"

"That's the going rate, mate," the driver scowled suspiciously at Ziggy. Keeping his composure, Ziggy annoyingly retrieved the pen and paper he kept on him in case someone spoke and I did not catch it; he could write it down for me.

"May I have your name and license number, please?"

The driver's thick, black eyebrows raised into a question, "What for?"

"Oh, nothing really. My friend, Craig Wilkinson is the Deputy Commissioner. I think he might be interested to find out that some of the city drivers are swindling tourists."

I nodded in agreement, although I had not the faintest idea what Ziggy and the driver were talking about, but the driver's face seemed to go pale while he contemplated what to do next.

We climbed out of the cab and Ziggy pulled out his wallet, "Forgive my feeble memory. Can you tell me again how much for the fare?"

"It's free," the driver mumbled resentfully, pedaling away into the night.

Ziggy explained the interchange he and the driver had, and we watched the rickshaw disappear, laughing until we could barely breathe.

"And Maamaan thought we could not take care of ourselves."

Two more glorious days in London, next stop: the beautiful City of Lights.

15

PARIS WAS *TRÈS ELEGANT* and proved to be everything I had read about and imagined. This sprawling metropolis known for its mix of classical and Renaissance aesthetics was simply stunning. With our very limited time, it was not possible to see all the museums and sites that we wanted to visit, so we selected a few customary tourist attractions that we had always heard so much about.

Our residence for our stay, the chic Hotel Banke, was a convenient twenty-minute walk to the Louvre, and only a three-minute stroll to the Grand Synagogue, where tonight Maamaan wanted to celebrate Shabbat.

The 125-year-old *Synagogue de la Victoire* mercifully survived the destruction by the Nazis during their occupation. Also called The Grand Synagogue of Paris, its grandeur was evidenced by its classical arches and 2,000-seat capacity. As we passed through its ancient doors, a Hebrew inscription above the entrance read:

This is none other than the House of God, the very gateway to Heaven.

Venturing further into the sanctuary, we were welcomed by the twelve tribes of Israel depicted in stunning stained glass. I found myself transported to an incredibly holy place. This Shabbat would be extraordinarily unique and would stay with me for a lifetime.

The familiar Hebrew service began in the early evening. We seated ourselves at the rear of the sanctuary in order to fully appreciate the expanse of the room. A red ceremonious canopy framed the elaborate dais, with matching red velvet benches in the surrounding balcony.

After the service, Esther and David Cofe, and their son, Cameron, old friends of my parents, invited us to join them for Shabbat dinner in the large dining hall. Maamaan seemed so serene conversing in rapid French with her friends who had immigrated to France several years ago.

As we sat together eating our chicken, Ziggy curiously asked, "Why did you leave Iran?"

Esther said, "Incipient unrest had begun to influence the many positive reforms the Shah had implemented, and we feared an Islamic revolution was building and would put our lives in danger."

I was not surprised to hear this, especially after my experiences with campus unrest at Shiraz and Goli's encounter with radicals at Vakil Bazaar. While I nibbled at my dinner, I theorized about the repercussions of a revolution. Would my family stay or would we become refugees? Was another purpose for this trip to find a new home?

Cameron, the Cofe's seventeen-year-old son, shyly tapped my arm. I smiled politely at the teenager whose long shaggy brown hair was pulled back into a ponytail.

"My mother tells me you will be staying for a couple days. Would you like a tour guide?"

"That is very sweet of you," I said. "But Maamaan speaks fluent French and she is familiar with the city. Early tomorrow morning we have plans to visit Notre-Dame Cathedral and then later in the afternoon we are going to the Louvre. I appreciate your offer, but we leave early Sunday morning, and there is not enough time to take in other sites. Perhaps during our next visit?"

Disappointment spread across his face and then he switched gears and began asking me endless questions about Tehran and college life at Shiraz. His lips were difficult to read, and his breath was repellent as if he had neglected his teeth for too long, making it difficult to concentrate on what he was saying.

On the walk back to the hotel, Ziggy had been uncharacteristically somber. As we arrived at the revolving doors to the plush lobby he asked, "Zhila, does your deafness make you feel like an outsider?"

It occurred to me that maybe he had an epiphany at the difficulty switching between languages and drew a parallel to my deafness. I was acutely touched by his empathy and maturity.

"Sometimes," I said, with a lump rising in my throat.

He quickly suppressed sympathetic tears, hastily wiping away one that escaped while I pretended not to notice.

The next morning, Maamaan and I meticulously dressed in stylish summer clothes. After all, we were in the fashion capital of the world. Ziggy was still sleeping, and we wanted to avoid the long lines at the Cathedral, so we quietly slipped out for a quick continental breakfast at our hotel.

We decided to forego the two-kilometer walk to the Cathedral and use the subway instead, waiting with a large crowd in a long, cavernous tunnel. A loud squealing noise echoing through the tunnel signaled that the train was approaching. When the doors of the silver train opened, Maamaan and I hurried into the nearest car, but it was filled to capacity, so we stood hanging on to an overhead rail.

The musky smell of people permeated the car and assaulted our senses. As the subway took off, a man crowded next to me, holding onto a dangling strap, took full advantage of every lurch of the train to press himself into my body. I tried repositioning myself, but the tightly packed crowd made it impossible. His repulsive garlic breath made me want to wretch as he exhaled into my hair. Coincident with the next opportunistic lurch I felt a hard thrust against my backside. Revolted by this deviant, I did some thrusting of my own, ramming my elbow deep into his ribs. When the doors flew open at our station, the pervert pushed his way out the door and slinked away. I said nothing to Maamaan about my French initiation, and scanned the area to make sure he wasn't following us. No need to taint her day over an ignorant degenerate.

Maamaan scurried about, taking pictures at the Cathedral — a treasure of French Gothic style. She translated the plaques, and taught me all she knew about its history.

"Zhila, did you know the coronation of Napoleon took place here in 1804?"

"Really?" I feigned interest, still a bit preoccupied with subway guy, hoping my jab broke a rib.

She pointed to a plaque, "It says General Charles de Gaulle's Requiem Mass was held here two years ago."

"Sorry we missed it," I said.

Strolling back to the hotel to pick up Ziggy for our Louvre excursion, I thought I had caught a glimpse of a ponytailed boy scurrying behind some nearby trees. Was I being paranoid from my recent incident, or was Cameron Cofe following us?

Ziggy and I walked behind Maamaan to the museum, and I discreetly told him about the disgusting creep in the subway, but surprisingly he laughed.

"You think that is funny?" I asked incredulously. "Why are men so loathsome?"

"It is biology," he said offhandedly. "Men tend to be endlessly aroused, but the majority of us only fantasize about doing anything like that."

I playfully punched his arm and said, "In that case, keep an eye out for Cameron Cofe, I think he is stalking me."

The Louvre offered more art and relics than we could possibly see, so we chose the sections that piqued our curiosity. We strolled around marble sculptures, joking irreverently about the statues with various body parts missing, revealing the inhumanity of passing time.

Ziggy pulled me behind a large white marble pillar and soundlessly moved his lips and pointed, "You were right. The Cofe kid is following us."

"What do we do now?" I asked.

"Ditch him, unless you want him tagging along all day."

I made a beeline to an amusing restroom sign with humorous pictures and arrows showing *Men to the left. Women to the right.* I ducked right, took advantage of the facilities and exited to find Ziggy patiently waiting for me.

We made a quick run through a passageway, meeting up with Maamaan, who was quietly admiring a sculpture of a bull in the Mesopotamian section.

"This place is breathtaking," she said. "There is nothing like this in Tehran."

I told her about Cameron following us and she discounted our suspicions. "He is most likely here for a school assignment."

I did not really care why he was there; I just knew that I did not want my day in Paris to be spoiled by a smelly teenager with endless questions.

After a perfectly apropos French dinner, Ziggy wanted to climb to the top of the Eiffel Tower.

Maamaan said, "I did that years ago with your father, you go and have fun. I will stay here for a while and enjoy my espresso and listen to the music."

I insisted on taking a cab after such a long day on my feet and, within fifteen minutes, we arrived at the base of the iconic tower. I looked up, straining to see the top.

"Are you sure you want to climb the entire thing?" I plucked a pamphlet off a rack written in Farsi. "There are three hundred steps just to the first level and about three hundred and five meters to the top."

Ziggy's eyes widened, "Let's give it a try."

He began at a quick pace up the steps in front of me, stopping frequently to allow those descending to pass. They appreciated his courtesy, but I knew his politeness was actually fatigue. At the first observation area, we simultaneously saw the elevator, then looked at each other.

"I thought you wanted to climb to the top?" I teased.

"Yes," but I realized I should have more consideration for my oldest sister," he jeered, as the elevator door slid open.

I could not have been more relieved as my back was sending painful reminders to abandon this climb.

Looking out over the spectacular panorama left us dumbstruck. "Look at the teeny little boats drifting down the river!" I blurted out.

We watched as pinpoint lights snapped on, one after another and twilight began to steal the day from the Champs-Elysees. I could not imagine there being a more beautiful avenue anywhere else in the world. I pulled my sweater closer against the chilly night air and we silently watched in awe as The City of Lights came to life.

After a long look at the city from above, we touched down on firm ground, and I turned for a last look up the majestic tower outlined in twinkling lights. Ziggy ran over to look at a display in a shop window while I stood at the crosswalk waiting for the light to change.

A car slowed, and two loud hoodlums rolled down their windows, gesturing wildly at me adding an ear-splitting whistle before racing away.

When Ziggy returned, I said indignantly, "Did you see that?"

Ziggy laughed. "You are a beautiful woman, Zhila. What do you expect?"

"Respect!" I said. "Simple respect!" Perhaps Israeli men would exhibit more sophistication and class.

16

NEITHER ENGLAND NOR FRANCE offered the level of comfort that I felt in Israel. It was pure serenity. When our plane touched down at Ben Gurion Airport, everyone aboard simultaneously began singing *Hatikvah,* the Israeli national anthem, as if it were customary practice.

As long as the heart within,
A Jewish soul still yearns,
And onward, towards the ends of the east
An eye still gazes toward Zion.
Our hope is not yet lost
The hope of two thousand years old,
To be a free nation in our land,
The land of Zion and Jerusalem.

I got chills and wept.

In Iran, we were ridiculed for being *nijes* — the unclean — but here, in our ancestral homeland, we were accepted inherently as kindred. I was so anxious to experience all of Israel's people and treasures, although four days was certainly not enough time to do that.

Uncle Joe, my father's brother-in-law, met us at the airport, but instead of taking us to a hotel, he told Maamaan firmly, "You will be our guests in Rishon L'Zion." Before Maamaan could protest, he politely cut her off, "Simi and I insist."

Uncle Joe, a tall, lean man with close-cropped, black hair, greying at the temples, adroitly pulled into the driveway next to a modest, two-story house. A man of about twenty-five, tall and broad-shouldered, stood on the porch waving and grinning.

"Meet your cousin, Joshua," Uncle Joe announced proudly.

He looked nothing like Joe and Simi, of course, because he had been born to parents who were murdered by Nazis near the end of their imprisonment in the death camps of the Holocaust. My aunt and uncle heard about this miracle baby and adopted him.

Cousin Leah came out to greet us with open arms, cheek kissing and hugs all around. I realized she must have known about my deafness, because she looked directly at me while speaking, enunciating each syllable. "It is so wonderful to see you again cousin. After you unpack, meet me in the backyard. We can play in the sandbox," she joked, referring to earlier times that we could barely remember.

Early the next morning, Joshua joined me for breakfast at the kitchen table. "Ready for your day in Jerusalem?"

At the welcome party celebrating our arrival the previous night, he had insisted on being my tour guide, and I eagerly accepted his offer. Ziggy paired up with Leah for the day and Simi would accompany Maamaan while she took care of some business for Papa.

We boarded a bus heading to the Tel Aviv central bus depot, where we transferred to a second bus. We settled in for the final leg of our ride to the Yad Vashem memorial, almost 70 kilometers away in Jerusalem.

"Last night you promised you would tell me the story of your early life," I reminded him.

He nodded solemnly. "I was too young to remember, so I will tell you the story that Abba told me: I was born in April of 1945 in the Buchenwald concentration camp near Weimar, Germany. Nazi guards shot my father, and my mother died during my birth."

I watched tears well up in my cousin's eyes as he paused to regain his composure.

"Two days after I was born," he resumed, "an underground resistance organization seized control of the camp to prevent guards from executing anyone else as they retreated. I was one of 20,000 prisoners liberated by the Americans."

"How did you get from Germany to Israel?" I asked.

"The nurse caring for me arranged for the Red Cross in Oslo to take me. The Red Cross contacted their Israeli counterpart in Tel Aviv, Magen David Adom. Their symbol is a red Star of David, instead of a red cross, by the way."

"Makes sense," I said. "Go on."

"Your aunt and uncle wanted to adopt a baby, and after hearing about me, they flew to Oslo, and brought me home. My first memory of them was splashing Maamaan Simi in the Mediterranean Sea."

We stepped out of the comfort of the air-conditioned bus into the suffocating humidity of central Jerusalem. We purchased tickets and entered into the world of the beautiful, sadness of Yad Vashem, the renowned World Holocaust Remembrance Center.

Despite having been educated in these atrocities by my parents, I was not even minimally prepared for the hard reality of the countless photos, names, and heartbreaking accounts of this genocide. It humanized the inhumanity. The fusion of emotions rushing through me moment to moment was almost disabling. Juxtaposed against this mind-numbing brutality, thank God, were the inspiring stories of heroism of righteous gentiles.

During the tour, Joshua was quiet, his broad shoulders slumped, and his usual happy face, solemn. A much-needed change of mood, away from the moribund reminder of Joshua's roots, came at the Zion Gate — one of the nine entrances into the Old City. This walled area within the modern city of Jerusalem measured almost a square kilometer.

Joshua smiled, grabbed my hand, and came alive. "Come on," he said, "Our first stop will be the Western Wall."

"This is the remnant of a retaining wall from the ancient Second Temple," he explained. "It looks out over a plaza in the Jewish Quarter. See over there the men facing the wall and praying? After the 1948 Arab-Israeli War, we were expelled from the Old City. All of this," he gestured, "was occupied by Jordan."

"How did we get it back?" I asked.

"I was one of dozens of paratroopers who landed in this plaza on June 7, 1967, to take back our city from the Arabs. Once we recaptured the Old City, the Jerusalem Brigade joined us to capture Judea, Gush, Etzion, and Hebron," he said, pointing in the direction of each city.

I looked into his huge brown eyes. "Were you frightened?"

Joshua's olive complexion reddened. "Sure, but we were all very determined. You saw what zealots did to us in Europe. My entire family was exterminated like vermin. Ours was a single-minded effort to ensure this would never happen again. We were not only fighting for Israel, but for all humanity."

The day flew by as we wandered through shops reminding me of Vakil Bazaar in Shiraz. In my periphery, I noticed Joshua occasionally staring at me and, whenever we crossed a street, he protectively grabbed my hand.

"What do you do when you are not entertaining family from Persia?" I asked.

"I walk through museums, explore World Heritage sites like Masada and the caves of Bet Guvrin National Park."

"But what about work?"

"That is my work," he answered, "I am a tour guide."

"Bringing me to Jerusalem must have been tedious for you."

He gazed at me with a gratified expression. "It is fun seeing the city through your eyes. The excitement and newness of it all is expressed in your body language; your enthusiasm brings new life to the experience for me."

We continued getting to know each other on the bus ride back home. He was so easy to talk to, and the time passed too quickly. I was a little sad to glance out the window and see a blue sign that read: *Tel Aviv-Yafo 5 km.*

Joshua tapped me on my shoulder, "Where would you like to go tomorrow?"

"What do you suggest?"

"I was thinking of taking you to Masada. It is an old fortress that overlooks the Dead Sea. The view is sensational; it makes you feel dizzyingly free. But I was also thinking of taking you to The Dead Sea."

I clapped. "Yes, that! I have always wanted to swim in the Dead Sea. It is a geologist's heaven! Besides, if it is this hot again tomorrow, swimming would be preferable to hiking."

I took quick advantage and switched roles to show off my slight knowledge. "Did you know that the Dead Sea is 429 meters below sea level, the lowest land point on Earth?"

"I did not know that," Joshua said with a wink.

"I guess my degree was worth something," I teased and continued in my best professorial voice. "The mineral concentrations are nine times greater than any ocean. Their deposits make it one of the world's saltiest inland lakes. There! End of lecture!"

Joshua continued our trivia game, countering with, "I will see your Dead Sea and raise you a Masada. Its rocky plateau has a commanding view of the Dead Sea, and in 73 AD, Jewish zealots committed mass suicide rather than submit to Roman rule."

I remarked mockingly, "Oh gosh, suicide trumps salt deposits. You win."

The next day, after twenty-five minutes on the road, we parked at Kalia Beach, on the north shore, and strolled hand-in-hand to a terrace above the beach. The view revealed a stunning display of the sea's turquoise waters surrounded by a backdrop of the golden-brown Judaean Mountains.

I covered my head with a scarf to inhibit the relentless heat. Joshua followed suit, donning his Tilley hat.

"Come on," I said, "I want the full Dead Sea experience."

Swiftly descending the staircase down to the beach, I noticed salt deposits covering boulders on the shore and on rocks in the water, making organic life nearly impossible.

Joshua said, "I know you do not hear well, but just so you know, this place is eerily quiet. If you look around, things seem motionless: no birds, no greenery blowing in the wind." As we walked to the water, he added, "The only sound now is the crushing noise of pebbles under our feet." He was becoming my human hearing aid and, although I found it somewhat charming, his running commentary was also a tad bit annoying.

The temperature was warm, creating a comfortable ease into the water. Joshua followed as I reclined onto my back, floating effortlessly on the surface.

Getting back onto my feet again presented an altogether different challenge, similar to unencumbering oneself from a waterbed. Joshua laughed as he lent his professional tour-guide hand to pull me upright.

I got salt in my eyes and, as I tried wiping them, I made the stinging worse. Now I was deaf and blind as tears cascaded down my cheeks. Joshua led me back to the cooler, where he kept bottled water and flushed the salt from my eyes.

"You okay?" he asked.

"Yes, much better thanks. I should have known better," I said sheepishly.

We sat down in a shaded area to keep cool, and I said, "I wanted to come here mostly because of the mud. The minerals in the salt and mud are known for their healing powers, so I wanted to test it out."

Joshua nodded and pointed to our left. "The mud is over there." Then he pointed in the opposite direction and said, "Meet me at that bar over there in an hour. Okay?"

It was nice to be on my own for a while and I hurried in the direction of the healing mud. I was cautiously hopeful that the therapeutic mud would help resolve the pain in my back and leg from my old accident.

Out of necessity, I ignored the stench of the sulfur drifting up from the mud besieging my nose. Pretending that I was being pampered at the spa, I smeared the cool sludge over me like a full body facial and lay in the sun to dry. Once the mud completely dried and my skin tightened, I felt as though I was trapped in a body cast. I hobbled to the water, keeping my eyes shut this time, and soaked until most of the mud rehydrated and fell from my skin. I used an outdoor guest shower to remove the stubborn remnants and then went hunting for Joshua.

I found him nursing a cocktail at The Lowest Bar in the World, speaking Hebrew to a man sitting beside him.

As I approached, he said, "Hey, Zhila, meet my good friend Yakov. He is also a tour guide."

The petite man flashed a gap-toothed smile and I grinned back. Farsi was not one of his languages, which limited our conversation to Hebrew, so I excused myself and left the men to talk. Finding a chair in the shade, I sat down to relax. I ran my hand down my arms and was amazed at how soft my skin felt; it actually glowed. Pleased with the results, I was optimistic that my old injury would be less of a nuisance.

It was of little consequence to me that Joshua was a drinker, but it was very important that the special man in my life abstain from alcohol. I detest the smell and the effect it has on people, not to mention the social problems it creates. On the occasion that my father came home after drinking too much, my innate response was to shrink from this stranger and avoid him until he sobered back to himself.

I wished we could have stayed longer. Israel was a magnificent country. As we touched down, home again in Iran, sweet memories of this glorious trip were thrust aside as my mind started racing with all the things I needed to do to prepare for my new job.

Those moments when I took time to reflect on this extraordinary adventure, I was overcome with enormous gratitude to my parents for such a generous graduation gift. It was not only a dream come true, but I had matured. I was more street-wise, actually more world-wise, and felt ready for my new job at Geo Tehran.

17

IN THE MORNING WHEN I AWOKE, the room was blessedly silent, but also an annoying blur. While I lay in bed stretching my muscles awake, I plucked my glasses from their customary perch on the table next to my bed. Swirls of black and beige instantly took on definition as the wallpaper came into focus, a delightful occurrence. Not so with my hearing aid.

I had purchased my hearing aid a year after I was hired at Geo Tehran. In the years since my first visit to the audiologist as a child, technology has improved, and I had renewed hope that my new aid would reduce the effort and strain of communicating. The harsh reality was a double-edged sword presenting a new set of effort and strains, although the hearing aid has been a tremendous benefit at work for meetings and conferences.

Before nestling it in into my ear, I hear sounds that I can only describe as distant rattling or rhythmic thuds. But once it is in place, a cacophony of sound assaults my brain from multiple directions: Zanna's music, quarreling voices, traffic — a seemingly endless juggernaut of racket. How do people deal with such ceaseless commotion?

After my second year at Geo Tehran, my employer recognized my aptitude, and added more responsibility to my duties training new recruits. I was rewarded with a private office and a nice raise. The future seemed gloriously promising.

Four years later, my world collapsed. The Shah was forced into exile and Ruhollah Khomeini returned in triumph to rule. The Iranian Revolution had an exhaustive grip, and the Jews of Iran began to leave *en masse*.

Demonstrations raged in the city center protesting a variety of social ills and complaints. The protestors carried an assortment of placards publicizing their demands; the most frightening emphasized their hatred of Jews: *Wipe out the Zionist State!* It was becoming clear that our life was going to change dramatically, and we were likely in significant danger.

Our worst fears materialized at the beginning of April when the country was seized by radical Islamists. The quasi-monarchy it had overthrown had expressed at least a modicum of tolerance for Jews living among them, but that indulgence had now vanished. I watched from my office window, looking down on Jamshid Avenue as demonstrations turned to violent turmoil with beatings, intimidation, and death.

One morning, while sitting at the kitchen table having my usual modest breakfast before work, Maamaan handed me the newspaper mumbling, "Turn to page three."

Her face so grave I was compelled to obey, but at the same time resisting the impulse to flee out the door to work. I nervously thumbed to page three.

A photo of the body of a man lying in a pool of blood was featured, a despotic admonition confirming who was in control. The caption under the photo included the name of the unfortunate victim: *Habib Elghanian* ... I could read no further as anguish consumed my soul. On the ground lay Uncle Habib, a dear family friend, his bare torso riddled with bullets. It was a clear message to those who dared to support the previous regime, Israel, or worse — a Jew.

I screamed, "How could they be so evil?!" I wadded the paper and threw it to the floor, covered my face sobbing uncontrollably.

Maamaan retrieved the paper and flattened out the wrinkles, "There is more," she said softly putting her gentle hand to my cheek. She handed me the page with a listing of names and said faintly, "Your friend is here."

As the emerging regime took power, they began executing about 150 dissidents daily, publishing their names. I grabbed the page from her and there, printed under the headline, "Counter Revolutionaries" was a quote: *Leftist and secular groups are not tolerated in the Islamic Republic.*

I quickly scanned the names and instantly my body went limp. I could not catch my breath and thought I would faint as the blood drained from my face: *Fayaad Dardashti.* The shock overwhelmed my mind and it stopped processing. This could not be possible! This must be a horrible mistake.

"I told him he must be careful. Why did he not listen?" I sat completely despondent and in shock, incapable of channeling my rage and despair.

By the last decade, Iran's Jewish population had increased to more than a hundred thousand. Now we were an endangered species to be slaughtered at will. Neither Uncle Habib nor Fayaad deserved this level of unmitigated evil. They were kind, gentle, and loving. How could this happen? Our beautiful country had plunged into complete madness.

My sweet, sweet Fayaad and Uncle Habib's senseless murders shook me to my core. I could not speak. I could not eat. I could not think. I did not go to work for the first time in seven years.

A few weeks after these senseless atrocities, Ziggy breathlessly bolted into the kitchen speaking so fast and crazed I could not understand what had happened.

As he caught his breath and calmed slightly, he said, "They broke into Papa's pharmacy, smashed everything and dragged him away!"

Hearing the commotion, my sisters came running into the kitchen. As we all tried to decipher what had happened, we looked into our mother's distraught eyes.

"What do we do?"

"For now, we wait," Maamaan said, as she took time to collect herself and formulate a plan.

Would there be no end to this derangement?

"Officer Sediqi!" I cried out. "Remember Officer Sediqi? He came when you called the police the time that Mr. Nuri threatened Julie with scissors, remember? He liked me. Maybe he can help us."

Without thinking it through, I shot out the door to the police station two blocks away.

Ziggy appeared at my side, panting, "Maamaan said do not do anything rash or stupid."

"Don't worry," I said, "We cannot attract unnecessary attention. We must keep calm."

The red brick building seemed harmless, but the marble entrance had an air of intimidation that made me pause and take a deep breath. Ziggy pushed open the heavy door and we cautiously entered into a dimly lit hallway, opening into a larger room with black-robed women working in tiny cubicles. At the far end of the room behind the information desk, sat my old friend, Officer Sediqi. He had aged appreciably, perhaps necessitating a desk job.

I approached tentatively, taking another deep breath and exhaling slowly.

Officer Sediqi looked up and a grin of recognition lit up his face, accentuating the laugh lines around his eyes. "I can't believe it!" he exclaimed. "Zhila! You are more beautiful than when I last saw you."

"And who is this young man?" he asked.

"My brother, Ziggy."

"What can I do for you today?"

I quietly said, "Our father was arrested this morning and dragged from his pharmacy. We need to find him. Would you know where he was taken?"

"I am so sorry. It is most probable they took him to Evin Prison," he said ominously.

My brother and I gasped. The name alone conjured up sheer terror. The prison was built at the foot of Alborz Mountains in the north and was notorious for mass hangings and torture.

"What did he do?" Officer Sediqi asked.

I tried to whisper, "Nothing, but he is Jewish."

"Then they probably think he is an Israeli spy."

"Papa would never do that. He is a pharmacist, a husband, and father. How can we find him? What do we do?" I pleaded.

Officer Sediqi moved a pile of papers to the side of his desk and leaned forward, speaking softly, "Not a thing! You would be arrested, too."

He motioned for us to come closer, and whispered, "I owe you a debt, Zhila. Had that man hurt his daughter, I never could have been forgiven. Your actions and reasoning that day were very courageous, and coming here for help, also brave. I have friends," he winked. "Give me your father's name and I will see what I can do."

"Solomon Shirazi."

Officer Sediq's eyes widened with recognition. "He is the owner of Farvardin Pharmacy on Daneshgah Jang Boulevard."

"Do you know him?" Ziggy asked.

"Very well. He's a kind man. He would make a terrible spy." Tears welled in Sediqi's eyes. "I will talk to my friends. If your father is alive, they will do their best to get him out and I will personally deliver him to you."

As Ziggy was about to give the officer our address, he waved him off. "No need, young man, I clearly remember where you live," he said, winking at me.

On the walk home, Ziggy said, "I have heard rumors at school about professors and their associates disappearing for speaking out against the new regime — no one ever sees them again. That is why the prison has been nicknamed Evin University. Trials are held without lawyers; the accused are found guilty of fictitious crimes based on forged evidence."

"What happens to them?"

Ziggy hung his head, hardly able to reply. "They are condemned to death."

The sun hastily dropped behind the hills outside the city, creating an amber glow in the sky. This heavenly respite allowed my mind to momentarily stop racing with thoughts of what could happen.

I said a prayer.

"I pray that Officer Sediqi reaches his friends in time," I said to Ziggy, horror sweeping through me at the thought of how quickly this could all go wrong.

We walked the two blocks home on heightened alert. The sun disappeared behind the mountain that sheltered Evin Prison, and we looked at each other with the same dire thought.

Would we ever see Papa again?

18

TRUE TO HIS WORD, two days later, Officer Sediqi appeared on our doorstep propping up our severely battered Papa. As I opened the door, there was a moment of pause when my mind and the visual needed time to connect, to make sense of what stood before me. As the immediate shock cleared, I covered my mouth to muffle my horror.

"PAPA!" I screamed.

Ziggy charged to the porch to help as Papa crumpled to the floor, no longer able to assist the officer to keep him on his feet. His singular intention, coupled with his last shred of vitality, was the force that got him home.

His nose was broken; his teeth were missing. The smell of rotting flesh testified to the torture he had miraculously, albeit barely, survived. His discolored, swollen face was marked with numerous wounds and gashes. And then he opened his eyes — his once beautiful eyes were milky white. They had blinded him. The stark reality of what lie ahead for us had collapsed at our feet. The twisted righteousness of this regime unequivocally exhibited, here on our porch, that their evil knew no bounds. Their perverted and depraved morality, sanctioned by their God, had no limit.

Maamaan slumped in a chair, her sobs slowly turned into a full-throated wail.

Ziggy and Sediqi carried Papa upstairs where they drew a hot bath.

Dr. Marcus arrived within the hour, "Where is he?"

Maamaan led the doctor up the stairs to the bedroom where he lay sleeping. Dr. Marcus sat next to the bed and gently touched Papa's cheek. He awoke instantly with a frightened start.

"It is Dr. Marcus," he said softly, "Sol, I hear those bastards gave you a hard time."

Papa nodded.

We solemnly clustered together downstairs anxiously to hear Dr. Marcus' report.

"I addressed his broken nose and cleaned his wounds. I put medication in his eyes to prevent infection, but there is nothing more I can do to restore his vision. It appears these monsters used acid to permanently blind him. He will need to see a dentist when he is strong enough. I will leave this medication for you to administer. Please follow the directions. What he needs most now is rest and quiet. If you have concerns, call me. If his infections worsen, take him immediately to the hospital. They will contact me."

The oppressive regime continued systematically torturing and murdering countless numbers of those adjudicated as dissidents: Jews, journalists, human rights activists, educators — anyone they deemed would "compromise national security."

Months passed before Papa could bring himself to talk about the incident at Evin Prison, being careful to leave out the grim details that he knew would upset us. He began slowly, at the dinner table one evening, carefully parsing his words.

"They forced their way behind the counter at the pharmacy, handcuffed and blindfolded me and threw me into a car. They put me in a long hallway with other prisoners while armed guards watched us. We did not know where we were or why, and no one was allowed to move or speak. We unfortunately found that out when a young man was bashed in the head with a rifle butt for whispering to another prisoner. We waited in the hallway not knowing what to expect or what would happen."

He stopped, suddenly overwhelmed by the agonizing memories. We sat silent while he regained his composure.

"Hours later, they stood me up and marched me to a room where a wiry, mean-looking man with a Hitler mustache, and stringy brown hair, sat at a table. He said he knew I was spying for Israel, and insisted that I sign a confession. I told him I was a simple neighborhood pharmacist, but of course he did not care if it were true or not. When I refused to sign the confession, a guard took me to an underground room where I fully expected them to kill me. It did not occur to me that they would do it slowly. All I could think about was how much I loved you all and how I would miss you. I considered telling them what they wanted to hear, but I knew in my heart that there was no way to appease them: admit I was a spy, I was a dead man; refuse to admit it, I was a dead man. I will never tell you the details of what happened. It serves no purpose and you saw the results — that is sufficient."

Maamaan wiped away the tears as they began to roll down his cheeks and said, "That is enough. You need to rest."

"But the most beautiful moment of my life," he continued, "although wrapped in suffering, came with my freedom — knowing I would be reunited with my beloved family when Officer Sediqi, my brother for life, said he was taking me home. "

We tearfully sat around the family table consumed by our father's torment, and faced with the stark awareness that next would come the intolerable discussion of our exit from the country we loved, and it would have to be soon.

19

INSANITY, FED ON THE UBIQUITOUS TYRANNY around us, morphed into chaos. It was impossible to keep track of the players while sifting through the propaganda to separate truth from fiction. The country's turmoil gave rise to a new oppressor to capitalize on our civil unrest, calculating when and where to pounce.

The dictator of neighboring Iraq sent his military troops to seize control of Iran's economy via the oil-producing region of the country. The resistance was fierce, and the invading army was ultimately forced to retreat, but not before countless lives were lost — a despicable and wretched commentary on the intentions of our leaders and how human life was so easily expendable. Throughout history, it has been the rare case where the benefits of war have surpassed the astounding destruction. My heart breaks at the devastating result of fascism on an innocent nation and culture. The toll it takes on humanity for generations is incalculable, and it is wholly unfathomable why peace is such an alien concept to those who seize control.

I picked up the rock I kept on my desk that I had found years ago in the Alborz Mountains, and tossed it to Mr. Jalali, my new recruit. "How would you determine the age of this rock?"

"I would need to see the formation it was picked from."

"Good. How is the age of formation determined?"

Mr. Jalali's voice was vibrant, and his lips thick and easy to read, as he said, "The geologic time scale …"

The building began to tremble and the air raid siren screamed out, cutting him off mid-sentence. As had become our company habit, my coworkers and I jumped to our feet and headed for the safety of the shelter.

"We will have to finish this later," I said. "We must go!"

From our fifth-floor perch, we rapidly filed down the stairs joining the nervous confluence of those from the upper floors, down to the basement.

As the bomb struck, plaster and dust billowed throughout the shelter. We covered our faces, suppressing screams and whimpers through the second explosion. We calculated the attack to be several blocks away, but the subsequent blast seemed closer.

Trying to appear casual, as if this was a harmless concern, I said, "Well, your first day at Geo Tehran will be memorable, would you agree, Mr. Jalali?"

He nodded nervously.

"Your résumé is impressive, and I am confident you will be an asset to our staff. Tomorrow, after the dust has settled, we can continue your orientation. Is that okay with you?"

He nodded again.

The Islamic Revolution had ushered in a dark era for Jews. Synchronized with the fighting between Iran and Iraq for control of the oil fields, the propaganda machine intensified. Jews were now accused of plotting with Iraq to thieve the country's treasure and flyers were circulated throughout Tehran encouraging vengeance against us.

The new constitution of the Islamic Republic mandated: *Jews are a minority ruled by Islamic law.* The laws were restrictive and set a nuanced undercurrent to goad brutality. If a Muslim converted to Judaism or married a Jew, the death sentence would be invoked. The inheritance laws stated that if a Jew converted to Islam, he automatically inherited the assets of his extended family. Consequently, if a family member had amoral tendencies, he could impoverish his entire family.

The evening of the bombing, when I walked through the front door of my home, Maamaan tearfully greeted me. "Thank God you are okay Zhila! News reports said there was a bombing near your work. Is that true?"

"Yes, we spent some time in the shelter, but the blast seemed to be several blocks away."

"That is too close," Papa warned.

Maamaan drew the blackout drapes in the kitchen and lit candles. We gathered around the table finally forced to discuss decisions that we had too long delayed.

The flickering light made reading anyone's lips a challenge, so I leaned in closer as Papa said, "People in the streets are yelling '*death to Israel*' and '*death to America*'. Many Jews are closing their bank accounts, selling their property and businesses, and leaving for countries in Europe, Israel, and the United States."

Aunt Sabra and her children had moved to America and reports were that she had bought a beautiful home in an area of southern California called Encino. After the fall of the Shah, she lost most of her investments and was forced to sell the house she had promised to me upon her death. Her virtuous promise, in light of the new circumstance of our lives, was now sadly moot.

Aunt Rebecca and her family, along with Uncle Izzy and his new wife, weary of living in constant danger, packed up and moved. The catalyst for their decision was the execution of their Rabbi, Yedidia Shofet, after he was accused of spying. Their peace-loving

Rabbi had worked tirelessly to demonstrate to the regime that Jews and Muslims could be brothers; his reward was death.

Goli was blessed to fall in love with an American and moved to Hawaii. And Fayaad, my sweet first love, had been executed — a memory that I still cannot face; it crushes my soul to vapor. The only thing left for me in this slaughterhouse was my beloved work and I had hope that I could resume my career in a place where I was welcome.

"I received this yesterday and I believe it will help to lighten the mood," Ziggy said standing in front of the refrigerator, waving an open envelope. Zanna popped out of her seat and grabbed it from him.

"It is from the University of Gothenburg in Sweden." She pulled out the letter and scanned it quickly and squealed, "Oh, my God! Ziggy has been accepted to their medical school!"

"*Mazel Tov!*" Everyone yelled, accompanied with a round of hugs.

"We must celebrate," Papa said.

"Better to celebrate in Gothenburg," Ziggy said. "I have been thinking that I will go first and establish residency, and then each of you can join me."

"Goli said she could sponsor me to immigrate to the United States, but first I would have to move to another country to qualify for a medical visa. Going to Sweden with Ziggy would work out perfectly for me," I said hopefully.

"Then Zandra could go next," Papa said.

Zandra shook her head. "No, Sam wants to stay here."

She had graduated with her degree and was running the pharmacy. Sam, her boyfriend, held an odd power over her that none of us quite understood. He seemed to be somewhat of an opportunist and not a suitable mate. Our worry was that he might influence her to sell the family business and give him the money — which, from everything we had seen, was a real possibility.

"But what do *you* want, Zandra?" Papa asked.

"I am hopeful that the pharmacy does well and I can stay. If not, I can always join Zhila or Ziggy."

Papa worried that Zandra was not facing the actual level of danger she would be confronting, and that Sam was taking advantage of her naiveté to manipulate the harsh reality.

Papa looked in Zanna's direction, "And you, Zanna? Have you thought of what you want to do?"

She and I had talked about her future extensively. Her boyfriend, Lassi, had graduated from optometry school and set up an office in the city. He was determined to stay.

"I will finish university in the spring and have already started applying to dental programs. I am at the top of my class at Tehran University, so I think I have a good chance of being accepted either to continue there or possibly at Shahid Beheshti Dental School."

"Are they accepting Jews?" Papa asked, urging her to look at the truth.

"A few," Zanna squirmed uncomfortably.

"You do realize the sacrifices you would have to make to live here? You will never be allowed a normal life: always watching over your shoulder for danger, always hiding that you are a Jew," Papa warned.

The hopeful fantasy of youth triumphed over facts, and she mumbled, "I know, but I do not want to leave Lassi."

Maamaan had been thoughtfully quiet, sipping her tea and listening intently. She finally spoke in a hushed voice, "And you?" She asked my father, "What do you want?"

"I am old and broken. It is hard to learn new things in my state. Being blinded, I now have more appreciation for your deafness, Zhila. The thought of living without my whole family around me intensifies my pain. Our country has been taken over by madmen, and they see us as a scourge to eradicate. My personal scars are a constant reminder of the depths of evil within this regime. Zanna and Zandra I pray that my suffering will not have been in vain and will serve to change your minds. I pray to

God you will. Leaving my home is the hardest thing I will ever have to do other than having to bury any of my children. I am frightened to leave, but I am more frightened to stay."

• • •

A few months later, I was able to secure a Visitors Residence Permit from the Swedish Embassy in Tehran, and booked a flight to Gothenburg where Ziggy awaited my arrival.

He was doing well in his medical school classes, requiring most of his time and attention. Goli and her husband had happily agreed to be my sponsor, so I kept busy with all the preparations needed for my eventual immigration to America.

It would take nearly six months to acquire my visa, and four months more for a green card, allowing me the better part of a year to learn English. I spent my days immersed in my new language at the Berlitz Language Center. After class, I would rush home to prepare dinner for Ziggy, during which I insisted on torturing him with my new English skills so that I could practice.

The mercurial passing of time seemed to disguise the reality of what I was holding in my hand. The day I had been preparing for so diligently had finally materialized. I held the physical product of my efforts, and its substance held my future. I studied my green card — which, in actuality, was pink — and longed to foresee my destiny. It pulled me into a dissonant collision of emotions difficult to reconcile. I wanted to cling to Ziggy, holding tightly to the protective comfort I had enjoyed in our year together. At the same time, I had to push forward if I wanted any kind of future for myself. It was extraordinarily daunting.

Within a week I boarded the plane to Los Angeles filled with countless misgivings. Goodbyes of this nature are grueling, but the heart wrenching effect of this second farewell wasn't as punishing as when I had permanently left the country of my birth for Sweden.

Book Two

20

THE PLANE SLOWLY TAXIED TO A STOP and my heart started racing. Twelve hours earlier, I had been in Gothenberg waving goodbye to Ziggy, then fifty-five hundred miles later, here I was in America. The season was even the same. Could it really be this easy? Chills and butterflies took over my body in anticipation of setting eyes on my beautiful Aunt Sabra and my cousins after so long.

I retrieved my luggage from the carousel and placed them on a cart — I was struck by the poignant visual of my life represented by only two pathetic suitcases. I pushed the cart, following the crowd to customs, where the agent found everything in order, stamped my passport, and waved me through.

Next in the exhausting chain of logistics, I stood waiting with hundreds of bobbing heads and waving hands signaling to their loved ones. I elbowed my way through the crowd looking for Aunt Sabra. Had she changed so much that I did not recognize her? Was she delayed? I was worried that something awful must have happened or she would be here. The crowd of greeters slowly dwindled and my apprehension grew. I was alone … how would I reach her?

My anxiety worsened and tears fogged my vision, so I found a place to sit to stifle my growing panic. What were my options? The phone was obviously out, but I had an address and money, so I took a deep breath, straightened myself, and followed a group of people out of the terminal to hail a cab.

The sky was clear, and a warm breeze was blowing, as the driver merged onto a crowded five-lane freeway with more cars than I had ever seen traveling ostensibly to the same place. The overhead sign said 405 Freeway, going north.

After snaking through a pass, we topped a small mountain that opened to an expansive valley crisscrossed with long boulevards lined with tall, skinny palm trees. This was not at all what I expected — Tehran was an elegant garden by this bleak comparison.

The driver dropped me in front of a two-story condominium in a non-descript neighborhood — this could not be right; I double-checked the address. We had been told that Aunt Sabra lived in a luxurious house up on a hill with a spectacular view of the city, but this place had no resemblance to that description. The security door was ajar, so I asked the cab driver to wait while I slipped in and scanned the mailboxes for my aunt's name: *Sabra Hamdani, number 21.*

I dismissed my driver and took the elevator to the second floor and found number 21. I knocked and waited. I rang the bell, knocked again and waited.

Finally, the door opened and there stood a strange, burly man wearing nothing more than a thin towel around his waist. "Who are you?" he grumbled nastily.

Carefully looking at his face and summoning my best English I stated, "I am Zhila, niece to Sabra Hamdani. Is this her home?"

The ill-tempered man mumbled something I did not understand, pointed to a black leather couch and swaggered off, leaving me with questions I was afraid to ask.

I pulled my suitcases from the hallway into the apartment with nothing else to do but wait and wonder. From the window, I surveyed the street below looking for anything that I might recognize to give me comfort.

Suddenly the very familiar aroma of chicken soup filled my nostrils and my body relaxed. This was unquestionably Aunt Sabra's home. But where was she? I prayed I had not missed her at the airport. I fell asleep on the black couch I had been assigned, assaulted by unsettling dreams of frantic searching for my aunt while she also looked for me.

A hand softly touched my shoulder and as my eyes slowly opened and adjusted to the room, an older Aunt Sabra came into focus, smiled and said, "Welcome to America, sweet one."

Her long dark hair, now streaked with gray, was piled on her head. She gave me a warm, welcome hug and the cheek kisses I had missed so much. "I was not expecting you until tomorrow, forgive me. I am so sorry for such a careless mistake."

"Who is the man?" I pointed slyly, picking up a motion in the room.

"Oh yes, excuse my manners! Jorge, meet my niece, Zhila."

"Zhila, this is my friend, Jorge."

My aunt stood and asked, "Hungry?"

I nodded and my stomach agreed and we went to the kitchen.

"Is Jorge just a distraction?" I asked with a wink, not really expecting an answer. She acknowledged with a nervous laugh.

I devoured her luscious chicken soup, so reminiscent of home, and we caught up with the news from Iran.

Unspeakable hostilities persisted between Iran and Iraq. The populace had become predictably jaded by constant fear, consequently the death count simply became math; no relation to humanity was left.

"These wretched, self-important bastards are nothing more than pampered man-boys throwing tantrums, bullying each other until they can steal what they want," Aunt Sabra complained.

"Instead of throwing rocks at each other they throw bombs, bereft of the slightest concern. Their hubris, so grandiose, they coerce respect and claim they are beloved. I pray daily that these foul pigs will have to come before God to answer for their willful crimes, forcing us to flee. Sometimes I feel I cannot go on, locked in the despair of such a broken life …" she trailed off. "Enough pity party," she sighed. "We must get you settled."

She led me down a long hallway, turning into a plain room with three beds lined up like cots in an orphanage. A sliding glass door that opened to a balcony allowed light into the room. "You will be staying here with your cousins. Parry will be moving out in about three months and Joe … well, who knows?"

"I thought Joe was engaged."

"He is," said Aunt Sabra, "but he cannot seem to commit to a date. I would be a fool to believe there will be a marriage."

Parry and I had been good friends when we were younger, but during our teen years we went to different schools and neglected our close bond. Despite the distance, I had been keeping up with family affairs and knew she was planning her wedding after the Jewish Holy Days in the fall.

"What is Parry's fiancé like?" I asked.

"David is short, bald, and Jewish," Sabra stated flatly. "He seems nice enough, but they will never be rich on his teaching salary."

"America has made you cynical," I said.

She sighed. "You are right. Parry is happy with him, so I should just accept it and be happy for her."

The underlying messages hidden in that conversation were filled with mysteries, as is the tendency of my family. They tuck their secrets into small, dark crevices like prayers left in the Wailing Wall. My aunt was riddled with these mysteries — one, being Jorge.

"Do Parry and Joe know about Jorge?" I asked.

"No!" Aunt Sabra's face reddened with embarrassment. "And please say nothing."

"But they live here, how could they not know?"

"Jorge is only allowed here while Joe and Parry are at work."

"How did you meet him?" I pressed.

"He's my plumber," she said sheepishly, evading my eyes as she looked down at the stained wood table. Finally looking up at me, we broke into the laughter of shared understanding. "He has an adorable son, Danny, late 30s. You might like him."

"You are such a *matchmaker*! I am not even here a full day, and you are shamelessly trying to make a *shidduch*." Teasing her with a tinge of truth I said, "He is not even Jewish, is he?"

"But you are a young woman in a strange city," she taunted me.

"And I do not need protection!"

"Okay, okay!" she said, her palms facing me in an attempt to soothe my feigned indignation. "At least meet him. Who knows, you might even like him."

"No thank you! All my attention will be consumed with getting settled. I must become accustomed to America, get a job, improve my English … so many things to do it is overwhelming. And, you know that Maamaan and Papa will eventually decide to leave Iran and join us, so I must prepare for them, too. I certainly do not need — or want a *goyim* plumber's son getting in my way."

21

MY FIRST FOUR MONTHS IN AMERICA were intense, but filled with blessings. Assimilation was by no means an effortless process, and I was grateful to have family around me who had been through the experience to guide me and ease the confusion.

With good fortune, and many prayers later, I passed my driving test and received my official license. There was no effective mass transit in Los Angeles, which was remarkable for a city this large, and mobility was paramount for any kind of independence. Aunt Sabra replaced her six-year-old car with a new one and passed her old one down to me, with an added bonus: instruction in the art of freeway driving.

Joe had found me a job as a geologist, but the position was in San Diego, 120 miles away from my family. As much as I missed my beloved career, I would have to postpone that ambition until I was more secure.

Tehran was larger than Los Angeles, but negotiating such a wide area with even wider diversity and limited English would have been a daunting challenge, but I was without question very blessed. Before I left Stockholm, my precious aunt researched a variety of resources for me, and suggested as a first step that I enroll in classes at a nearby adult education center. I registered for their citizenship program that would relieve Goli of the sponsorship burden as soon as I passed the test and became a citizen. The course I signed up to take had an English language component, allowing me to continue my English instruction — another blessing: it was free!

My English teacher, Rosanna Canales, was magical. She was just a bit taller than my five-foot frame, with beautiful brown skin, long black hair and a heart of gold. She traversed well beyond the bounds of teacher and is someone to whom I will be forever grateful.

Realizing that my deafness would add another level of complexity to my efforts, Miss Canales showered me with extra instruction and one-on-one care. This attitude toward a disability was something that I did not know existed — no shame, no discomfort, no secrets. The subtle protective shell within which I had cloaked myself, suffered a slight tear, just enough for me to realize that this shield even existed. After only a few months in this country, from the genuine kindness of strangers, I began to experience a transformation that you could only designate as "an awakening."

Parry's wedding was simple, held in a small synagogue, with the reception at David's parent's home — exactly what she wanted. David proved to be a very kind man, graciously demonstrating caring, and respect for Parry, making sure that she maintained center stage throughout the wedding.

I noticed Joe across the room, alone, the perfect opportunity to talk to him about Sadie. "Aunt Sabra tells me you are having a difficult time committing," I teased. "Did Parry's beautiful ceremony urge you to finally set a date for your wedding, or are you completely unnerved now?"

Joe and Sadie met at a family Passover dinner and discovered they had much in common. They both were born and raised in

Iran, a good conversation starter, and Joe was instantly taken with her elegant beauty.

I was more cynical and suspected the family matchmaker at work again. "Did Aunt Sabra arrange for you to meet?"

"That never occurred to me," he mused. "I was so captivated by Sadie; she was all I could think of."

"Then what is your hesitation to marry?"

"Sadie insists on the old ways and wants to keep her family name. She is completely uncompromising and refuses to speak about it further," Joe lamented.

I was thoroughly confused by my cousin's foolish remarks. "But that is our custom; you would certainly expect her to feel that way. How could that possibly bother you?"

"This is the United States, and it is very important to me that we observe the customs of the country that welcomed us openly without hostility. The custom here is that women take the last name of their husband. I like that practice very much; it shows respect." His voice grew louder with each word, making my hearing aid tickle my ear with its vibration.

"This is why you hesitate?"

"Yes, I want my wife and children to take the Hamdani name."

I tried reasoning with him. "Respect goes both ways, you know. She thinks differently about this than you. Have you ever asked her why it is important to her?"

"We have argued endlessly about it, to no avail," he said.

"Arguing and discussing have nothing in common," I replied, a bit irritated with his stubbornness. "How do you plan to resolve this?"

"Pure deceit," he said a bit prideful, laced with embarrassment.

"Perfect," I said sarcastically, "The first building block of every marriage should be deception. 'The bigger the lie, the better', makes for a strong foundation."

"Your sermons make me thirsty," he said. "I am going to the bar."

My classes at the adult training center were going very well, so I decided it was time to learn a skill and find a job. As I perused the catalogue of classes at the career center, one stood out: *Long Term Care Nursing Assistant, $250.00.* It seemed like it might be a good fit especially since my parents were aging and, when they arrived in California, I would know how to care for them and make their lives more comfortable. My English had improved enough, and my ability to lip read English was coming along surprisingly well, so I felt confident that I could follow the course work.

After class, as the other students were leaving, I shared my plan with Miss Canales. "Zhila, I think this is a wonderful idea! May I suggest another class too? Across the street is a community college that offers American Sign Language. I think you would enjoy it, especially since language seems to come more easily to you than many people I've taught. The instructor is a very lovely deaf woman, who can offer you her personal perspective and acquaint you with the deaf world. It would also increase your English vocabulary."

I trusted Miss Canales completely and took her advice, enrolling in the beginning level evening class, while studying my nursing course during the day. She was entirely correct about my new deaf teacher, Stephanie.

Although our deaf experiences were of two very different worlds, Stephanie and I bonded through our similarities. She taught me that those "similarities" had a designation: Deaf Culture. Within the culture, her background allocated her to what was referred to as capital D — *D*eaf, because she was a member of a community with a shared language forming the basis of their culture. It is an empowered collective with an impressive history, storytelling, art — embracing all the necessary elements that comprise a culture. I, on the other hand, given my background, hold the designation of lower case d — *d*eaf, because even though I was deaf just like Stephanie, my community was among hearing people whose sphere was strictly auditory. They spoke, and I read their lips to survive within that culture.

It was an abnormal notion to me that disability could be accompanied by a culture. My indoctrination had been purely one of shame, so this legitimizing concept of disability would require some adjustment. I was excited to explore all the aspects of this American version.

• • •

Joe and Sadie's October wedding was lavish, taking place at a hotel with a seven-course dinner and a large band. The music was excessively loud, so I removed my hearing aid for some blessed silence. While Sadie greeted guests, I took the opportunity to talk to Joe.

"How goes the duplicitous life? You are now officially married, so I assume whatever Einstein plan you devised was a success."

"Yes, but please keep this between you and me only. If Sadie were to ever find out, she would not forgive me," he confessed.

I scolded, "Is there no end to the covert nature of this family?" He justified his exploit insisting that it was *the only way*, and disclosed his undercover, genius plot.

"Sadie and I had been looking for a house to buy, but we were not finding anything that she liked. Then recently, Susan, our realtor, showed us a large four bedroom one with a pool and big closets that came on the market, and Sadie fell in love with it.

Mocking him I said, "So you bribed her with a house?"

"No. Better, I bribed Susan. I paid her extra commission to convince Sadie that the sellers of this house were a very devout couple and would only sell to a married couple. Susan created a superb story assuring Sadie that the only way to satisfy these very pious sellers was to show them a marriage license proving a *union in the eyes of God*. Then she added a brilliant aside, taking full advantage of Sadie's naiveté, and said, 'Of course in this day and age, it is widely acceptable for people to live together without marriage, so I will advise you that both names on the marriage certificate must be the same or it will be suspect to these God-fearing Christians."

"What people will do for money," I said with contempt.

"There's more," he continued, "We went to city hall, got married by a judge, and, with license in hand, we were approved *in the eyes of God* for purchase. Escrow closes in 20 days."

I looked at him in disbelief. "You got married twice?"

"Yes, it is *win-win*! And twice as likely to last, right?" He joked. "Now I am off to the bar to get a drink to assuage my guilt."

I drifted off with thoughts of the kind of marriage I envisioned, and the qualities of the man I wanted to share my life with. It certainly was not *Joe style*, and I left the wedding feeling quite disillusioned in matters of love.

22

I PASSED MY NURSING CLASSES and my state exam and officially became a Certified Nursing Assistant, authorizing me to start my job search. My first assignment was Mrs. Kellerman, an elderly, irritable woman confined to a wheel chair. She suffered from diabetes and obesity, with all the associated medical difficulties, but mostly she had a chronic case of the sorrows. I was assigned to her for a nine-hour day, six very long days per week, requiring an enormous amount of patience and tongue biting.

She had a nasty disposition, and it seemed the only enjoyment she derived was barking orders at her minions to do her bidding. It quickly became apparent why she had no friends, and her children avoided her as if she were a rattlesnake.

While I cleaned the breakfast dishes one morning, Mrs. Kellerman rolled her wheelchair up next to me at the sink, as I looked out the window at the park across the street. I was deep in thought about a letter I had received from Papa, when suddenly a screeching Mrs. Kellerman interrupted me. All thoughts of my parents instantly disappeared from my mind.

"What do you think you're doing?"

I placed a clean plate in the dish rack, smiled at a dog catching a high-flying Frisbee in the park and then looked over at Mrs. Kellerman's cold blue eyes.

"The dishes," I said, feigning a sweet smile.

I had promised myself that I would not get upset with the old woman, even though my first impulse was to squirt her curly white head with dish soap. Anyone this surly must be dealing with hidden pain and an excess of regrets — a testament to her slumping shoulders and mean nature.

"There are too many suds in that sink!" She pointed to the detergent bottle, held up her index finger, and said, "Just one drop!" I restrained a laugh as she wheeled out of the kitchen at full speed.

I returned to thoughts of Papa's letter advising me that they would be arriving in California within a year, asking me to secure an apartment for them. I had just found a small flat for myself, two blocks from Aunt Sabra, in the hopes that my parents would be able to move into the same building. The apartment manager agreed to let me know when one of the apartments was vacated.

The duties of my job were similar to that of a glorified maid — as remote from geology as one could possibly trek. In addition to housekeeping and laundry, I helped Mrs. Kellerman with her personal hygiene, always checking for any bruising or injuries, and assisted with her frequent medical appointments.

Unwinding after work was essential to quell the remnants of Mrs. Kellerman's constant badgering. I worked out at the gym, and did yoga three nights a week at a local studio, to purge her criticism from my body.

After a particularly difficult day, I rolled up my yoga mat and looked up to see a rather handsome, Latino man standing over me grinning, "You're Zhila, right?" He was an exact copy of Aunt Sabra's boyfriend, Jorge, only a younger version.

I nodded. "You seem to have me at a disadvantage."

"Your aunt showed me your picture and told me I'd see you here."

I stood, extended my hand, and said, "You must be Danny."

As the other students left class, Danny stayed, directly stating the reason for his unusual social visit.

"Have dinner with me tonight. I'd like to get to know you."

He was a bit overweight with light brown skin, but his smile and kind brown eyes suggested he might be worthy of consideration.

We dined at a local Italian restaurant with no break in the conversation. He spoke slowly and looked at me while speaking so it was obvious that my aunt had coached him about my deafness. He was a registered nurse at a nearby Medical Center, so it was easy to talk about our common work. He spoke kindly about his patients, and seemed like a sensitive person, attentive when I spoke.

As our date was coming to its end, he asked, "Would you like to catch a movie sometime?"

"If you do not mind seeing a foreign film. I rely on the subtitles," I said, taking my keys from my purse.

"Right, I'll look into that. How about …" he paused before finishing, "Friday night?"

"No, I have Shabbat dinner with my family every Friday evening."

"Shabbat?"

"It is a religious observance."

"Oh, okay, how about Saturday night?"

"Maybe. Look for me at the gym and I will let you know."

I got into my car and sped off leaving him wondering without a definite commitment.

I wrote to my parents and siblings about Danny. Each one strongly urging me to break it off before it got serious.

"He is not Jewish, he is not Persian, he will never understand you …"

Three months after my infatuation over our Italian dinner, we married at city hall.

Regretfully, two very long years later, the enchantment came to a crashing disenchantment — a cautionary tale of domestic abuse worthy of warning. Oh, that I had heeded my family's sage counsel.

23

OUR FIRST YEAR TOGETHER WAS WONDERFUL. Danny was affectionate and generous, bringing me gifts and surprising me with flowers. He made a very sweet and sincere gesture to understand my background and traditions by purchasing a book about Jewish customs and history. He was always interested in hearing about my problems with Mrs. Kellerman, especially after a particularly challenging day. If I seemed exasperated, he would take a break from whatever sport he was watching on TV, sit up attentively ready to hear what had upset me.

"Hard day?" he would ask.

"I try everything I can think of to make Mrs. Kellerman's life more tolerable," I complained. "I polished her nails and, when I finished, she criticized the shade. I held up the bottle and asked, 'Is this the color you requested?'"

Danny interrupted, teasing me by transforming himself into a whining Mrs. Kellerman, "No, that's the wrong one!"

"Exactly!" I laughed at his silliness and continued my story. "There was no point quarreling with her, so to end her tantrum I said, 'Perhaps you'd like to choose another color and we can start again?' She waved me off like an annoying fly and rolled away, clicked on the TV and sulked for the rest of the afternoon."

Danny and I could always laugh together at our shared experiences with cranky patients, and my mood lightened while we planned dinner.

It was a quiet afternoon when I had the occasion to meet Mrs. Kellerman's daughter, Linda. She dropped in for a short visit — coincidentally timed with her mother's nap, no doubt arranged to avoid her irritable disposition. She was about fifteen years older than me, with dyed strawberry blonde hair that contrasted strangely with her dark complexion. We sat at the kitchen table sipping tea and munching on sweet biscuits.

"Growing up with her," Linda pointed in the direction of her mother's bedroom, "was not easy."

I nodded knowingly. "I can imagine."

"She was extremely critical of everything I did. If I got an 'A-minus' on a test, she'd slam me for not studying harder. I remember winning first prize in a piano competition; I was so proud and excited. Know what she said?" I shook my head.

"You played lousy and the others played worse."

I covered my gaping mouth. How could anyone talk to a child that way?

"I was sandwiched between two dreadful parents: an abusive, drunken father, and a mother who was a belittling bitch, impossible to satisfy."

Mrs. Kellerman had never mentioned her husband to me, so I tacitly nodded, encouraging Linda to tell me more.

"Did my mother ever tell you how she ended up in that wheelchair?"

"No." I lifted my cup of steaming tea and took a sip, bracing myself for what she was going to divulge.

"I had just returned home from college for Thanksgiving. Dad was drunk as usual, and I heard them arguing as they were coming down the stairs. He was behind her and she turned looking up at him and said something about sobering up before the guests arrived. He took exception to that and told her to fuck off and pushed her. She fell almost the full flight of stairs. We rushed her to the hospital, but even after multiple surgeries there was nothing more they could do. The accident, if you can call it that, intensified her bitterness — if that was even possible. Her happiest day since was the day my father died, but even then, she bitched that his death wasn't agonizing enough."

"Oh, my God!" I said, "That explains a lot."

Linda nodded, "I thought you should know. She has several nurses, but she only talks about you, Zhila. I know she probably doesn't show it in any way, but believe me, she is really fond of you."

Tears welled up in my eyes and Linda smiled. "You thought she hated you, didn't you?" I nodded and Linda reached for my hand and gave it a squeeze. "Trust me, I know exactly how you feel."

I was excited to tell Danny about my conversation with Linda, but when I arrived home, he was lying on the sofa engrossed in a basketball game, making it clear he was not interested in conversation. At first, I was hurt, and a warning bell went off in my head. Is he tired of me already? Is this normal? Then I rejected my good instincts to escape the truth and scolded myself: *I was selfish for interrupting his game. I cannot expect to be the center of his world all the time. My expectations were unrealistic. Maybe he had a hard day and needed some personal time. I should be more understanding.* I mentally catalogued all the reasons that made me a horrible wife deserving this treatment, but I could not shake off the nagging feeling that something was not right.

Over the next few months, Danny grew distant, so when my doctor told me I was pregnant, I thought it must be divine providence. I had the naive illusion that telling him that he was going to be a father would change everything: he would look into my eyes with deep affection, take me in his arms, and our romance would be rekindled.

I took a deep breath, put the key in the lock and found Danny in his usual place on the sofa watching sports. I sat down next to him, wrapped my arms lovingly around his neck and kissed him.

"What's that for?" he asked.

"We are going to have a baby," I answered dreamily.

He sat very still and unresponsive while my words sunk in. Then his deadpan response left me wondering if he was teasing or not. "Who's the father?"

I punched his arm. "You, silly."

He feigned a scrap of interest, but it was apparent that this was not in his plans. He sat frozen, calculating how to free himself from this trap. His reaction neither fit my fantasy nor sweet memories of how doting Papa had been when Maamaan was pregnant with Zanna, and my world crashed.

My intuition was exactly right. Danny acted out his vile drama to ensure a righteous escape. I had been replaced by alcohol and my *services were no longer needed.* He might as well have displayed a neon sign in our home: *Danny Is No Longer Accessible or Attainable and is Available.*

His moods were acutely erratic, so I avoided him, never knowing from each moment if I would be invisible or repulsive. He habitually came home late after drowning his sorrows at some dive bar, and fell into bed as if he lived alone.

I finally reached my breaking point of rejection and decided to wait up for him after his next exploit. I accosted him as he stepped through the front door and unloaded weeks of repressed emotion attacking his manhood.

"You are a pathetic excuse for a man! You stay out late, and have the audacity to come home to your pregnant wife reeking of booze and cigarettes and the god-awful stench of cheap perfume. You are a defective soulless, lump of steaming waste!"

"Get away from me bitch!" he said, pushing me so hard I lost my balance and fell.

Nothing is more humiliating than lying on the floor, staring directly into the face of your most foolish mistake. I let this happen, allowing this barbarian into my life. The exact life I swore, after Joe's wedding, that I would never accept was exactly mine. Here I was, in what should have been the most fulfilling time of my life, feeling completely despondent and broken.

Crying myself to sleep, thinking life could not possibly get worse, a sharp, ominous, pain stabbed me awake and I knew something was terribly wrong. Within minutes, paramedics arrived and confirmed my worst fear: "Ma'am, we're very sorry, but you have lost your pregnancy."

In the next room, through it all, in a drunken coma, slept the no-more-father-to-be. From the bottom of his countless tequila bottles, my besotted husband's desperate prayers to Jose Cuervo were answered.

I returned to Mrs. Kellerman's a few days later and, noticing my miserable mood, she queried me. "You've been gone and now you aren't your overbearing, cheery self. What's the matter with you?"

The floodgates crashed open and, through the wracking sobs, my entire heartbreaking crisis gushed out.

"He's a selfish monster, Zhila. Kick him out before you end up like me."

"Maybe he will change," I mumbled hopefully.

Of course, Danny did not change. Instead, he got worse. When he was not preoccupied in some mindless sport on TV, he was unaccounted for. I had been downgraded to roommate.

Since opening up to Mrs. Kellerman, she had softened and insisted I start calling her Nancy. We had actually become friends, and I understood her on a much different level, and had come to love her. She was still a crotchety old lady, but she was my crotchety old lady.

I had taken an earlier shift, arriving before Mrs. Kellerman awoke. The night nurse and I went through the obligatory shift change procedure and all was well, so I began making breakfast. I knew Mrs. Kellerman loved waking up to the smell of bacon, so I got busy. As the aroma of breakfast started moving through the house, I expected to see the flashing light we had set up for her to signal the nurses. No light — that was odd; my concern sent me running.

She appeared to be sleeping, so in a singsong voice I said, "Nancy … Bacon …"

Nothing — not even a twitch.

I placed a hand on her forehead. She was cold. Shaking, I went to the other side of the bed and saw that her face had turned the gray-green of death. I began to cry while checking for a pulse but, as I already knew, life had left her debilitated body.

I hurried to the neighbor's home and asked them to call the paramedics, letting them know that Mrs. Kellerman had passed. I did the required paperwork in a daze and, while the paramedics and police took care of Nancy, Linda and I comforted each other promising to meet again at the funeral.

I went directly home; the comfort of my bed was all I could think about. Funny, the blinds were drawn; I thought I had opened them when I left this morning. I glanced over and my bed was unmade. Strange I know that I made … There lay Danny, asleep with his very own distraction spooned next to him.

I ripped the sheet from their naked bodies, threw open the blinds and shouted, "GET OUT!"

They hopelessly tried to cover themselves while he made weak, cliché excuses.

"GET OUT!" In homage to Nancy, I calmly informed him, "Your things will be packed and on the curb Monday for trash pick-up. I suggest you get there before they do."

An eerie serenity came over me. A weight had lifted; I had regained a particle of control over my life and reclaimed my freedom.

Over the weeks, I was launched into an uncontrollable roller coaster ride, fiercely dragged into a traumatic inventory of my life. I found myself negotiating the mine-field of all the loses I had suffered — deafness, accidents, Fayaad, so many deaths, my homeland, my dreams, miscarriage, marriage. Each appraisal leaving me more battered than the last, pushing me deep into a pit of despair. I took time off and stayed in bed, filled with shame, blame, and regret.

My pity party came to its eventual end. Just when I thought I could no longer withstand wallowing in my own degradation, I somehow experienced an epiphany. I do not know how or why, but just as the Phoenix arose from the ash, my respite allowed me the time I needed to regroup and get reacquainted with the person I lost in this horror of a marriage. I was finally empowered to action, so Joe recommended a divorce attorney, authorizing the next step to legally rid myself of this loathsome imposter of a husband. Six months later — lesson learned. Good riddance Danny Boy — Hello to a new decade, 1990!

24

ON THE FIRST DAY OF SUMMER, my parents finally arrived in Los Angeles after not having seen them for five agonizing years. Preparing to pick them up from the airport, I anxiously looked over my checklist, considering which route to take. I had not yet developed enough confidence driving the freeways — too many things could go wrong — so ruled that out. Surface streets were slower, but I did not want to take any chances on my parents being stranded and alone as I was when I arrived.

Maamaan's face lit up when she spotted me waving from the crowded railing. Fortunately, she was not able to see the shock on my face as she and Papa walked the ramp from customs. Maamaan had not changed much, except her hair was shorter with more gray than when I last saw her, but sadly, Papa seemed to have aged a quarter of a century.

I walked briskly through the crowd to meet them and Maamaan grabbed me and hugged me so tightly I could barely breathe. Papa stood in front of me as I let his hands roam over my face.

Yes, Papa, it is me, Zhila."

He laughed through the tears pouring down his cheeks beneath his dark glasses.

When my neighbor moved out, I arranged for my parents to have the apartment next to mine. It gave me such relief to have them so close by and I took a week off work, before starting my new assignment, to help them settle in. As Maamaan unpacked, I showed her the list of things they still needed that I had not yet gotten.

Papa immediately found the Persian radio station that broadcast in Farsi. It was both stabilizing and discomforting to get news from home, and the kitchen table became his secure base for that needed familiarity.

I took Maamaan to the local kosher market to help her get accustomed to the neighborhood and we shopped for dinner. We walked home and into the kitchen with arms full of groceries. met by an agitated Papa talking nonsense and gesturing for us to sit down.

"An earthquake hit northern Iran early this morning!"

My mother's gray eyes widened as she covered her mouth, "Oh, my God!"

I sat down. "How bad was it, Papa?"

"7.7 magnitude. We must make sure Zandra and Zanna are alright"

The death toll was 50,000 with 135,000 injured. The impact on my old neighborhood, thankfully, was negligible, but I thanked God that my parents were here with me, far from the devastation. We agonized over the desire to be there with my sisters, but also relieved not to be there. Anxiety was high. and we tried for the rest of the day to reach my sisters without luck.

The Iranian government refused a humanitarian offer of help from nearby Israel. Their righteousness dictated that thousands more die rather than accept any assistance from their enemy. They could not afford to let Israel appear compassionate and clung to their longstanding and needed loathing of anything Jewish. Their practice was to vilify Israel. no matter the cost. even if it was to their own detriment. Why be concerned with insignificant suffering and death when they could use the tragedy to exploit Israel?

We were finally relieved and thankful to reach Zandra at the pharmacy. Everyone was fine and survived the earthquake with little damage. At least we would be able to celebrate Shabbat with extra gratitude for everyone's safety. The pharmacy had sustained a little damage, but Zandra's marriage had suffered much worse.

Maamaan looked downcast during Shabbat dinner as if she was disgraced. She said, "As we have long suspected, Sam was not an honorable man. He came home from work in a terrible mood and was screaming at the children. Zandra demanded he stop. and he turned on her and broke her jaw. Maybe the stress and chaos of the earthquake became too much for him and he snapped or maybe this has been going on and Zandra has kept it to herself. It does not matter; this kind of behavior is dishonorable. and we want her to sell the pharmacy and come here."

Tears welled in my eyes. "My God, my heart breaks for her. Are there no honorable men left in this world?"

"Papa and Ziggy," Maamaan said with pride.

Papa smiled. "I hope there are more than that."

"How is she doing now?" I asked.

Maamaan said, "She has taken the children and separated from Sam and has agreed to put the pharmacy up for sale."

"Thank God! What about Zanna and Lassi?" I asked.

"They are not planning to leave Iran, but there is some good news in all this mess — Zanna is pregnant."

My eyes filled with tears. "Zanna is going to be a mother … so hard to believe she is old enough. I remember so clearly when she was born — plopped right into my arms, and now she will have her own baby." I looked away to hide my own disappointment and

"Is something wrong, Zhila-joon?"

"No," I lied, but surely my expression gave me away. I was already forty and the possibility of getting pregnant again was low. I changed the subject, "When will Zandra and the children get here?"

"As soon as the pharmacy sells and she makes all the arrangements. She and the children will stay here with us until they get settled."

Zandra's children, Chava and David, were already school age, and, sadly, I had never met them and had many lost years to make up.

"And more good news from Ziggy," Maamaan said. "He has been writing to an Orthodox woman from Iran who lives in the Los Angeles Jewish Quarter. He will be coming to Los Angeles this fall if things work out."

"Will they get married?"

"That is to be seen," Maamaan answered.

My parents were forced to navigate through a great deal of unfamiliar circumstances and activities worsened by Papa's nightmares of torture causing him sleepless nights. Maamaan had opted to sleep on the floor while Papa slept either on an air mattress or in the rocking chair in the living room, so thankfully she was getting some sleep. She had never been one to complain, and had her own ways of coping, so I did not want to probe and make her feel uncomfortable.

She appeared to be content with the sparse décor in the apartment, seeming disinterested in making a home as if she was secretly harboring a desire to return to Iran. Clearly, she yearned for home and my heart ached for her. I knew this move would be a painstaking struggle, likely why they had postponed it for so long. The ground was continuously moving beneath her, keeping her off balance in her own personal earthquake.

The family was finally reassembling, and soon our unit would be together again and safe just as Papa had prayed. Until that happened, I feared to hope or pray for my own happiness, warding off any possible disaster or curse. First, we must convince Zanna to make our family whole again.

25

MY NEW WORK ASSIGNMENT at the Jewish Home for the Aging was conveniently close to home. Since Maamaan and I would be helping Zandra with the children, this would make logistics so much simpler. I did not want to curse my luck, but everything seemed to be falling nicely into place.

One of my new charges was Mrs. Cohen, a compassionate, 92-year-old woman who had been living at the home for the last five years. I knocked on her door to check on her, but there was no answer, so I used my key to let myself in. The tiny apartment seemed too still, so I glanced around the small living space and kitchen and then found her resting in the bedroom. As I moved closer to the bed, I noticed visible signs that she may have had a seizure: her face was too pale, and she was not breathing. I immediately began CPR while saying a quick prayer: *Please God, not again!*

In less than a minute, she regained consciousness, had a pulse and was breathing again. My heart was pounding, and I was shaking, but so very grateful that she was back with us.

Within a couple days Mrs. Cohen was released from the hospital, so I stopped by her room to see how she was doing.

Her daughter, Mamie, an enormous woman, threw her arms around me swallowing me in a long, appreciative embrace, before propelling me by the shoulders out in front of her, tearfully announcing, "You saved my mother's life!" She thrust a bouquet of beautiful roses into my hands and blurted out, "We owe you so much!"

• • •

Zandra sold the pharmacy pretty quickly, and she and the children arrived safely in Los Angeles in the fall. After a couple of months of adjustment, she settled into a home near us and immediately began preparing for her pharmacy licensure exam. Her English was getting better, although the process required a lot of time translating between Farsi and English.

We coordinated our schedules to maximize our time, ensuring that one of us was available to drop and pick up Chava and David from school. I was able to take night shifts when necessary, giving Zandra plenty of uninterrupted time to study during the day.

One day, I noticed Chava still sitting in front of my TV. I asked, "How many times have you watched that video?"

She held up five fingers on her left hand and one on her right, answering, "Only six." She paused the videotape and said, "Zhila, look!"

A scene from *The Wizard of Oz* started playing showing the Wicked Witch setting the Scarecrow on fire and Dorothy throwing a bucket of water on him to extinguish the flames, accidently splashing the witch.

"Look! She is melting!" Chava giggled, looking toward me. "Want to see it again?"

"Chava, I just thought of the perfect nickname for you."

This perfect angel of a child looked up at me with huge brown eyes, "Tell me!"

"Ozzie."

"Ozzie? Oh, from my *Oz* books. I love it!" She rushed over, hugged me and whispered, "But only you can call me that."

"Agreed."

David stormed through the front door noisily interrupting "Ozzie" time. He was two years younger and took advantage of every opportunity to torment Chava. She held one of her *Oz* books in her lap while watching the video and David jumped on the sofa, snatched the book from her and ran off to hide.

Just as Chava opened her mouth to protest his rude intrusion, I said, "It is okay Ozzie, I think I know where he went. I will retrieve your book while you finish your movie."

David had been misbehaving lately, probably due to the recent upheaval in the family, and he just needed a little attention with a lot of love and patience. He always ran into the kitchen to hide under the sink, so I called out his name several times, pretending I had no idea where he was and finally opened the cabinet doors greeted by the sweetest, toothless grin I had ever seen.

"Oh, my goodness, you are an excellent hider." He climbed out of his hideout giggling and I said, "If you give that book back to Chava nicely, I will play more hide-and-seek with you, okay?"

I adored spending time with the children; they brought me such joy. My favorite time was "homework club", held after school at my kitchen table.

"Finished!" David declared as he thrust his arithmetic assignment into my hands.

"Okay, if they are all correct, then it is movie time."

He squirmed and wiggled as I graded his paper, anxiously waiting. He did his best to focus on my pen strokes, eyes wide, while twisting in his chair.

I looked up at my nephew, whose mop of brown hair fell halfway to his shoulders. He sat straight up, folded his hands, and waited for the verdict.

"Perfect 100%, you are so smart," I said.

He ran whooping into the living room and took a flying leap onto the sofa. "I am a flying monkey!" he announced landing next to Chava.

"No time for silliness," I warned. "Soon I will take you home and then I must go to work."

Zandra was so involved in her books, she did not even hear us come into the house.

"How are your studies going?" I asked.

"You startled me!" Zandra said. As she relaxed, she added, "And remember to speak to me in English. You speak more clearly than most Americans I have met. I wish I could learn English as fast as the children," she whined. "And you. You are amazing! You have learned the language despite your deafness. You would think with perfect hearing, I could learn it easier."

"But you forget," I gently scolded her, "I started learning it in Gothenberg. I have been working on it longer than you, so it is not fair to make that comparison. It is one of the hardest languages to learn, so be kinder to yourself."

The children were bathed and ready for bed and. as I opened the door to leave, Zandra grabbed my hands and, in a rare demonstration of affection, said, "Thank you so much for all that you are doing. I do not think I could survive this without you." She hugged me tight and I left grinning like a flying monkey.

I clocked in for the night shift, and checked in with Karen, the RN on duty. "Poor Mrs. Stein was attacked by an intruder today," she whispered.

"Oh, my God! What happened?"

"A homeless woman crawled through her window, stole a basket of fruit, and some money."

"Was she hurt?" I asked.

"I heard she was just a bit shaken up. Here is your list of patients for the night and, to be safe, double check that their doors and windows are secure."

I was nearing the end of my shift as the sun was coming up and brought Mrs. Stein some coffee. “Good morning Zhila,” the frail woman greeted me as I handed her the java.

“Good morning, Mrs. Stein. I heard you had a visitor yesterday.”

“That poor woman,” Mrs. Stein sympathized. “She has to live on the streets. It’s a *shondah*!”

“I heard she stole your fruit basket.”

Mrs. Stein shook her head. “No, I gave it to her and $100.00. Now I have a new friend.”

I had misgivings about her friend-making strategy, and worried about what she may have started, so I documented her story in my daily report and clocked out. I was exhausted, but had plenty of time to sleep before picking up the children from school.

• • •

Ziggy joined us in America after finishing his medical residency at a Stockholm hospital. He was anxious to start his life with his fiancé, Vered, with whom he had been corresponding. We were all eager to meet her at a special Shabbat dinner. She grew up in southern Iran near my alma mater, Shiraz University.

She was a petit, olive-skinned woman with kind eyes that greeted me like a long-lost friend. “Zhila, we finally meet!” She threw her arms around me, gave me a squeeze, and kissed both my cheeks. “Ziggy has told me so much about you.”

“It is lovely to finally meet you as well. Come, sit next to me for dinner,” I said.

Maamaan opened the tiny table in the living room, added wooden extensions, and magically turned it into a table large enough for eight people. David carried to the table a bowl, almost as big as he was, filled with Shirazi salad to add to the delicious meal that Maamaan had prepared. It was a classic Persian feast, with all our favorite dishes designed to ease any discomfort Vered might have felt. Maamaan said the blessing and lit the Shabbat candles and Papa recited the wine blessing.

Just as Ziggy finished the blessing for the golden homemade challah bread, he raised his glass and announced, "Vered and I will be married in June."

A chorus of "*Mazel tov!*" echoed throughout the apartment.

• • •

Each of us had a task in the planning of Ziggy and Vered's elaborate wedding, filled with traditional Persian and Jewish rituals. After many toasts, and customary dancing and singing, Ziggy tapped his wine glass to quiet the room.

He stood on the dais as the music faded. "First and foremost, I would like to thank my parents and everyone who helped make our wedding so special, especially Vered for agreeing to be my wife. Our deepest gratitude to Vered's very gracious parents, who have given us a beautiful home near the ocean — a generosity that is more than we could ever repay. Thank you to everyone who graced us by sharing in this very special day. And lastly, I want you all to be the first to know that I am now officially Doctor Ziggy Shirazi, M.D. having passed all the necessary exams to practice medicine in the state of California."

A concert of voices shouted, "*Mazel tov!*", accompanied by thunderous clapping that I am sure must have reverberated throughout the hotel. The band started up to accentuate this momentous announcement and invited everyone to the dance floor to celebrate.

I sat down next to Maamaan to talk about Ziggy's wonderful news, and she said, "It gets even better," and pulled a letter from her purse. "It is from Zanna: They will be moving to Los Angeles in a few months."

I could hardly contain my joy, but a nagging, uneasy feeling disturbed me. *Why now? What had gone wrong?*

26

I HAD A LONG, DIFFICULT SHIFT AND WAS EXHAUSTED. I could not wait to lay my head on my pillow and dissolve into a sound sleep. I put my key in the lock and pushed the door open.

"SURPRISE!"

I nearly wet myself it scared me so badly, requiring a moment to get reoriented from the shock. Zanna wrapped her arms around me and squeezed then pulled away so I could see her speak.

"I have missed you so much," she sobbed.

Tears of joy poured down both our faces while we hugged again.

Lasi, who I would certainly not describe as Mr. Warmth, offered his hand, greeting me with a reserved, stiff handshake. "Good to see you, Zhila."

"You too, Lasi."

A fleeting, little head popped out from behind Zanna, then disappeared again into the folds of her plaid, cotton dress.

"And who is this?" I crouched down, pulled the material from his face and said, "Peek-a-boo!"

Joshua shyly giggled, let go of his mother with one arm, and gave me a half hug.

"My God Zanna, I cannot believe you are really here."

Maamaan, wiping the tears from her face, was having a hard time composing herself to speak. "Papa," she whispered trying to regain her voice, "do you believe this, the whole family is finally together again."

I took a couple of days off work to spend some time with Zanna. I knew that something was wrong, she seemed fragile and occasionally I would see her wince in pain.

"Zanna, it is a beautiful, sunny day, perfect for just the two of us to get out. There is a lovely park nearby, would you prefer to drive or walk?"

"Let's drive," she said grabbing her purse from the kitchen table. Los Encinos State Park was more than 100 years old, established for travelers along a 600-mile road connecting all twenty-one California missions. It was a relaxing place with the ideal ambiance for the conversation we were about to have.

We sat on a bench with a view of the small lake, watching ducks and geese float by, and I gently said, "You are not well, are you?"

Zanna began to tremble, and I held her in my arms waiting for the emotional storm to pass.

When she calmed, I pulled away and she dabbed her eyes and blew her nose. "I have breast cancer, Zhila. You know the medical treatment in Iran for a Jew is second-class at best, so Ziggy found me a doctor at UCLA Medical Center, and I have an appointment with him next week. Fortunately, the cancer is noninvasive and has not spread, from what they can tell."

I took her hand and we looked out over the lake. "Does this place remind you of Shahr Lake?"

"Yes, I remember we went there as kids. It is quite a bit smaller, but it makes me miss home an awful lot."

I changed the subject. "Let's get some lunch." I pointed to a restaurant across the lake. "Over there is Lakeside Café; their food is very California cuisine."

Over the winter months, Zanna and I spent a lot of time at the lake and the café while she coped with her cancer treatment. She had enormous resilience, strengthened by her love for Joshua. I learned invaluable lessons from her about the real meaning of courage, not only related to health issues, but on starting life over.

"I was accepted into UCLA's Dental program," Zanna announced during one of our lunches.

"But you are already a dentist. Are you doing advanced studies?"

"I am licensed in Iran, that counts for nothing here. I have to be licensed by an accredited body in this country and in California. Of course, my studies will go easily, since I am fairly fluent in English, and I already know the field, so I am not concerned."

I was so impressed with Zanna's zeal for life and her persistent fearlessness. She made it appear so easy, taking on life in full force and never complaining — compared to her slovenly husband: the exact opposite. He slept late, never stopped eating, and did nothing except whine and complain that he was too old to learn new ways, much less a new language.

"What is your insipid husband doing to help lighten your load?"

Zanna immediately detected the disgust in my voice. She glared at me, but then her face softened. "He is having difficulty adjusting, you should have more empathy."

"Why should I have empathy for a lazy slob? We have all gone through the same struggle to adjust and we did it. Why does he get special consideration?"

"Because if it were not for my cancer, he would never have left Iran. It is humiliating and my fault he is unhappy."

I did not want to start an argument, so I changed the subject and said, "Let's take a walk around the lake."

We walked around the water, watching the ducks and geese, and I knew there was something more Zanna was not saying. "There is something else on your mind. What is bothering you?" I asked.

"I was not telling you the truth when I told you I was going to Sacramento for that dental conference," she said shamefully. "My doctor strongly recommended that I have a mastectomy to lower the risk of the cancer becoming invasive and spreading, so I had the surgery."

I covered my mouth and held up two fingers.

Zanna nodded with tears streaming down her face. "Yes, both. Ziggy, Lasi, and now you, are the only ones who know, so promise me you will not tell anyone."

Here was our childhood indoctrination coming back again to torment us demanding that we never step outside the restrictive protocols of imperfection. Zanna learned early to whisper and lie about my deafness to avoid any possibility of our family being ostracized. She learned her lessons well and preferred to be a member of my club than burden our parents. This was a cultural aberration that unquestionably needed to change, although here I was complicit, agreeing to tell no one. I begrudgingly kept her secret while she studied and received chemo treatments, heartened only by Joshua joining our after-school homework club.

• • •

Aunt Sabra had heard on the radio about an organization called SHHH — Self Help for the Hard of Hearing — an educational support group for people with varied hearing losses and backgrounds. I imagined that attending a meeting might be a good way to meet people like myself, so I decided to go.

The Cochlear Implant was a topic that had fascinated me since moving to California, and the next SHHH meeting was going to have a speaker who would address everything we ever wanted to know about this mystifying subject. We met in a crowded room above a bank building, with a captionist who typed when anyone spoke, then it was displayed on a large screen.

The first speaker, a statuesque woman in her mid-40s, started off with the statement: "A CI does not cure deafness. Deafness is not a disease to be cured."

What a great start. Maybe we are not flawed and imperfect after all. She carefully explained what the implant was, and was not, expelling the myths and including the necessary technical points, risks and rewards, emphasizing that it was not practical for everyone.

The second speaker, who had the surgery to implant the device, talked about his personal experience. "I could hear perfectly until an illness robbed me of the hearing in my left ear," he tapped a round, piece of plastic near his ear, attached by a magnet to his greying head. "The biggest challenge I had with this was the struggle to get the processor adjusted properly to mimic sounds that I remembered. I preferred that my dog's bark did not sound like a sick duck and my wind chimes tinkled instead of clanked. It took eight months for my audiologist to modify the program to produce near normal sounds. My dog now sounds like a healthy duck."

The audience laughed and I mused ... Could I live with a quacking dog?

27

DEAFNESS CAN BE EXTREMELY LONELY, although I am blessed with exceptional lip-reading skills that allows me to understand about 60% of spoken language. The remaining 40% either does not show on the lips or looks the same as other letter combinations. I fill the gap using context and guesswork that is exhausting and often wrong.

Socializing with other deaf and hard-of-hearing people was a refreshing mental and physical respite from navigating the hearing world. The SHHH meetings provided a needed break from that daily strain with which we grappled. I counted the days leading up to the next meeting to indulge the simple shorthand one enjoys from a shared sameness.

Their holiday party was crowded by the time I arrived, but I managed to find a seat in the back. Along the perimeter of the room were tables filled with a wide array of favorite foods that members brought. I contributed a bowl of *Tahdig*, a saffron encrusted rice dish cooked with a crispy crust. The dish usually leaves the *nosher* wanting the recipe, so I have learned to bring printed copies to hand out.

While the announcements and acknowledgements were in progress, I looked up and noticed a bald, middle-aged man looking for a place to sit. As his gaze reached my section of the room, I pointed to the empty seat next to me. He had an engaging smile, and a charismatic energy that attracted me.

He sat down, looked me in the eyes and signed, "Thank you for being so friendly, this is my first time here." He fingerspelled his name, "M-I-C-K-E-Y D-A-N-I-E-L-S," then pointed at me and said, "And you?"

Trying to remember signs from the beginning class I had taken years earlier, I slowly signed back, "My name is Z-H-I-L-A S-H-I-R-A-Z-I. Nice to meet you."

Mickey had warm, empathetic eyes, and it struck me that this was the first time I could remember looking into eyes first, not at lips. I tried my best to tell him that my sign language was weak, because I had forgotten most of what I learned.

I asked, "Do you use your voice? I am a lip reader."

He nodded, speaking and signing at the same time and I was able to pick up that he was a sixth-grade teacher and had lost his hearing from a virus.

Abruptly, noise from a microphone filled the room interrupting our conversation. I noticed Mickey was having trouble with his aids, so I pointed to one and gestured, "Turn on your T-coil."

"What's that?" he asked.

This particular night, the organizers had installed *loop* technology in the room enabling a hearing aid to pick up sound more directly, improving the quality. I took one of his hearing aids from him and showed him the button, pushed it and handed it back to him. He put it in his ear and his eyes opened widely.

"I can hear so much better! Thank you, I can't believe I didn't know I had that feature," he said a little embarrassed.

"You are welcome. Shall we eat?"

Mickey hovered over my *Tahdig*, wondering what it was, so I told him that was my contribution to the party and explained what was in it. As he put a heaping serving on his plate, I noticed he was in marvelous physical condition and most likely worked out to stay in such seductive shape.

I finished filling my plate, and turned to continue our conversation, but he had turned away and was talking to a blonde woman wearing excessive make-up and rather revealing clothes, and I felt a little slighted.

As I was walking toward my seat to sit down and eat, Mickey got my attention and waved me over. "Z-H-I-L-A," he finger-spelled, "This is J-U-N-E. Maybe you already know each other. When did you lose your hearing, June?"

"I started having problems in college and over the years it has deteriorated."

"And you, Zhila, when did you notice your hearing loss?"

I was distracted for a moment when someone put the microphone next to the speaker and the music blared. "Sorry, it is really loud in here. I had meningitis as a toddler and it destroyed most of my hearing, so I did not grow up hearing."

The music stopped and the White Elephant gift exchange was announced to begin in five minutes. Each person had brought a used or joke gift and placed it under the Christmas tree in exchange for a number. When your number was called, you selected a gift, unwrapping it in front of the crowd.

Mickey answered to number 33 and, in disbelief, I noticed he selected the blue and white wrapped gift I had brought. I wondered — was he Jewish? He tore open the Chanukah wrap and held up my used, but functional teletypewriter to show the crowd his prize.

He looked over at June curiously, "Do you know what this is?"

She shook her head, highlighting her perfectly coiffed, blonde curls framing her ample cleavage spilling out of her hot, pink blouse. I rebuked myself for the jealous thoughts that uncontrollably popped into my mind. I had never been a jealous person. Where was this coming from?

I waved to get Mickey's attention and tried to sign, "That is a telephone for the deaf."

He came over next to me and I explained that it was teletypewriter used for a typed phone call to another person who also had the device.

I showed him how it worked, and his brown eyes sparkled. "I'm getting quite the deaf education tonight. My new deaf telephone will come in handy, but I will have to find someone else who has one," he hinted.

A security officer entered the room to warn us that we only had a few minutes before the building would close for the night.

Mickey walked me to my car, and under the streetlight said, "It was very nice meeting you. By the way," he pointed to his new teletypewriter, "Do you have one of these?"

"Actually, I had two. That one was mine."

His eyes smiled, "This is kismet you know — *beshert*! Now you are obligated to the divine powers to give me your phone number."

• • •

Three days later, the light on my teletypewriter flashed and I answered typing, "This is Zhila." GA.

"Hi, Zhila, this is Mickey, your new teletype kindred spirit." I waited for his signal for me to type back, and seeing nothing, I prompted him.

"Hi Mickey, so nice to hear from you, I am glad you called. When you finish your thought, type 'GA'. That means '*go ahead*', signaling me that you are finished typing and it is my turn." GA.

"I would like to properly thank you for my new machine. Would you like to go out for dinner Friday night?" GA.

"I cannot on Friday, I always have Sabbath dinner with my family on Fridays." GA

"So you're Jewish?" GA

"Yes, I am, is that a problem?" GA

"Not at all, I am Jewish too. We have more in common than I thought. How about Saturday night?" GA.

"I would like that very much." GA.

"Do you like Chinese?" GA.

"Love Chinese." GA.

"Wonderful, 7:00 p.m.? Do you know where Ping Pongs is?" GA.

"Yes, I will meet you there at 7:00. By the way, SK means '*stop keying*', the conversation is over and we can hang up. See you Saturday, thank you for calling, good night." SK

I had a date! I immediately reverted to an angst-ridden teenager worried about how I would look, what would I wear, what would I talk about, would he like me ... I had to stop this ridiculous adolescent behavior. I should just cancel.

I had some tea and settled my mind. I must really like this man to behave so foolishly and be so concerned with how he would view me. He must have liked me enough to want to get to know me, so Saturday night it is — Ping Pong, my heart.

28

I WAITED IN THE LOBBY OF PING PONGS, scanning my reflection in the lobby's full-length mirror. My black hair had grown quite a bit, and now hung past my shoulders. I had draped a beautiful white scarf around my new black dress, and paced nervously while I waited. I was one year short of 50, and had not had a successful relationship since Fayaad, and had not had a date since divorcing Danny — a pretty lousy record, but I was tired of being lonely and aimless. I had lost faith in my ability to judge men and that likely accounted for most of my nerves.

Mickey walked through the door and his kind smile was so genuine that my body instantly relaxed and I felt at ease.

"Hi Zhila! Am I late?"

"No, I think I was a bit early. Nerves, I guess. I have not been on a date in a long time."

"Well let's remedy that and order some *dim sum*. That always calms my nerves," he joked.

The restaurant was nearly empty, which seemed odd for a Saturday night, but we would be able to understand each other much easier without the interference of ambient noise. This seemed to be another positive sign that this was meant to be — *Beshert,* as Mickey described it in Yiddish.

We ordered dim sum to start — the restaurant's specialty — and then went a little crazy ordering everything that looked good.

"Tell me about your family," Mickey said.

"Where do you want me to begin?

"Let's start with where you grew up and how did you happen to come to Los Angeles?"

I told him about my life in Iran, and what it was like living there, especially being deaf and female. I found myself telling him everything about my schooling, Aunt Sabra and my family, and what happened to Papa in prison, and the reasons we had to leave. I felt so comfortable I could not stop talking, only interrupted when another course of food arrived. You cannot lip read and chew at the same time, so we had automatic breaks in between my story, but he never once looked disinterested, seemingly engrossed in my every word.

"I feel very self-conscious being such a chatterbox and dominating the entire conversation, so I will stop and you can tell me about you."

There was a long pause as Mickey took a bite of shrimp dripping in lobster sauce. "No, I think tonight should be about you," he said, "and our next date can be about me. We have too much to learn about each other in just one short night."

I teased him. "I think you are more interested in eating than talking. I do understand, though, because this food is delicious."

"Tell me more about your parents," he asked.

"I have spoken very little about Papa since his death two years ago and I do not want to start sobbing in my orange chicken, so I will keep this part short. Maamaan lives next door to me. She misses my father very much. He passed in his sleep from heart failure in 1998. I think she has had a much harder time adjusting to his death than she did uprooting her life and coming here. The regime completely sucked the vitality out of him, leaving him a silent, broken man. I think he lived as long as he did out of sheer will for Maamaan." I paused, my throat closing up as I suppressed my sobs; one lone tear sneaked out of my eye. "He was a wonderful, sweet man and now I must stop talking about him before I dissolve into a grief stricken, wailing puddle."

Mickey cautiously got up from the table and came over with his arms out. "Come here," he said gently as he wrapped his arms around me.

I melted in his embrace and fell in love. He held me close until we both remembered we were in public. We finished our meal, realizing our lives had drastically changed.

• • •

The new millennium arrived without the dreaded Y2K Millennium Bug wreaking havoc on the world's computers, as all the experts had predicted for at least a full year would happen. The administrator at work had fretted for months about the chaos that was coming that was sure to disrupt our records. We listened to endless lectures on what we would have to do before and after it happened. Then ... nothing happened and the world breathed a sigh of relief. I thanked God that I would never have to hear the term "Y2K bug" mentioned ever again.

Our second date was a lovely Saturday afternoon Shabbat picnic in the park.

Once settled in, Mickey said, "God graced me with two wonderful girls, which is a dream I've had since my early 20's. My oldest daughter is Aviva, a beautiful, 17-year-old, smart and levelheaded." Mickey's face glowed with pride. "I have no doubt that she will accomplish everything she sets her mind to."

"And your younger daughter?" I asked.

A huge smile took over his entire face. "Dalia is in a gifted fifth grade magnet program — so smart it is astounding. I have had primary custody of the girls since my divorce, and the girls became my world. We are always busy biking or hiking, and sometimes we go to the movies."

"Are you able to hear the dialogue in a movie?" I asked.

"Before my second hearing loss I could if I used special headphones. But now, nothing helps. It is no surprise, though. My doctor told me that my hearing would continue to deteriorate until I was completely deaf. That is the reason I enrolled in sign language classes at Pierce College."

"That is where I took my classes, too."

"To be honest," Mickey confessed, "I have a difficult time following a lot of what you say. It probably is a combination of your Persian accent and my lousy hearing aids. I would imagine I am not easy for you to lip read either."

My heart froze. This was a kiss off! He is going to tell me this our last date. I stared at him, like a deer in headlights, unable to move. He took off his Yankees cap and massaged his bald head. "I was wondering how you would feel about taking more sign language classes with me?"

My expression must have confused him because he quickly added, "You don't have to … I just thought it might help us communicate better."

I started laughing. "No, I said trying to compose myself … I thought you were breaking up with me. The look on my face was relief not refusal."

We both doubled up, laughing and babbling at the same time like teenagers.

"Let's have some more iced tea and toast to us."

Since I did not have much extra time for classes, we agreed for now that Mickey would enroll, and then once a week we would get together, and he would teach me what he had learned — after all he was a teacher and I was a good student.

• • •

Our relationship blossomed over the next few months. We enjoyed being together so much, and could not stop thinking of the other when we were apart. We tried new restaurants, went hiking, and our most favorite thing: subtitled foreign films. We always saved time after our activity for sign practice, and Mickey was a very patient teacher.

As we were leaving the theatre, after watching a very good French film, we decided to get some tea and dessert. We sat in a cute little bistro, waiting for our order, and I said, "You seem a little nervous?"

"I suppose I am. My mother will be visiting from Florida this weekend and I would really love for you to meet her."

"I would be honored to meet your mother."

"That is a relief! Sometimes meeting parents can be risky. How about lunch at Ping Pongs, 1:00, Saturday? Mom loves Chinese, too."

Vivian Daniels was a happy woman who seemed to have few regrets. She was in her mid-eighties with delicate ringlets of curly white hair and radiant blue eyes setting off her tanned, wrinkled face.

She insisted that I call her Vivie, and I spent the afternoon absorbed in her sweet stories of Mickey and his twin brother. She pointed at her son with a chopstick.

"This one was easy, but his twin brother … now he was a challenge. Put them together and you had trouble."

Mickey squirmed in his seat as I encouraged Vivie to tell me more.

"When Mickey was ten years old, there was an incident in our neighborhood. Some older boys were playing Cowboys and Indians, and they were indeed wild Indians."

"Oh my God, this is embarrassing," Mickey complained, "Do you have to tell Zhila this story?"

She shot him a look and he sat back.

"While on their bikes, those boys pedaled by this little black girl who lived down the block. She had a rare skin disease and was not able to grow hair, so she wore an inexpensive wig. One of the boys plucked the wig from her head as he rode by, tossing it to the other boy, leaving the girl crying in the street." She pointed a chopstick at Mickey, "This one ran down Rutland Road after the two Indian imposters, who had dropped the wig in the middle of the street and sped away. My sweet boy picked up the wig and returned it to the little girl and comforted her." Mickey blushed, "I was so proud of him, I could have burst."

She beamed at Mickey who grinned sheepishly back at her. "Excuse me," he signed, "Restroom."

When he stepped away, Vivie leaned forward conspiratorially. "My Mickey's has had a rough life. He deserves more than what he's gotten. He's too good. My son will give away the farm to help others. He loves you, Zhila. I suspect you know that already. His ex-wife, Rebecca, robbed him blind. You seem like a very sweet person. Promise me you will love my boy and treat him well?"

"I promise."

"Thank you! He's very sensitive. When his grandmother died, he was eleven years old. I never saw a child cry as he did. I think you're a good match for him. Aviva will be going to college before long, and Dalia will follow soon after, then he will be alone. Being a father means the world to him and, once they're away, I'm afraid he will be lost."

She paused, looked over my shoulder toward the restroom. "A loving couple is more than the sum of its parts. They are more powerful when they are together." She took my hand. "I'm so happy you love my son, and I can see clearly how much. Zhila, please be good to him." She squeezed my hand and quickly pulled away as Mickey approached.

I never saw Vivie again. A month later Mickey got a message while at work that she had died of a heart attack. Though I knew her only briefly, I fell in love with her. Being raised by such an outstanding woman made it plain why Mickey was so honest and caring. Keeping my promise would be the easiest thing I would ever have to do.

29

MICKEY'S HEARING CONTINUED TO DETERIORATE until it became too difficult to understand his students, making it impossible to continue to teach in a classroom. Hearing aid technology had not improved enough to remedy his loss, so, on the advice of his doctor, he retired from his beloved sixth grade class.

He had known for some time that this day was coming and, having a passion for writing, decided the timing must be providence. At 51, he knew this was not going to be easy, but I had become his inspiration for starting life over and complaining would be shameful after what he knew I had been through.

Mickey was very responsive to the activities that I enjoyed, and got such pleasure showing me new and interesting places. I had not spent much time exploring the Los Angeles area and there was much to see. He surprised me on our Saturday afternoon date with a tour of Descanso Gardens' sensational spring blooms. Iran had many beautiful gardens and Mickey knew that I missed them terribly.

We passed through the turnstile into a wonderland of meadows, woodlands, and chaparrals accentuated by flowers of every color.

Mickey signed, "Beautiful day," as we crossed an arched bridge into the Japanese garden with its characteristic teahouse surrounded by a koi-filled stream.

The cherry and plum trees were in full bloom. This was the perfect get-away to shed the week's frustrations.

"I would love to visit Japan," Mickey said dreamily. "Did I tell you that my BA degree is in Asian Studies?"

"You are a man of many dimensions. Maybe one day we can go to Japan together and you can show off your degree," I teased him.

We strolled hand-in-hand past the camellia garden and down a winding path around twisted oaks, stopping at Café Descanso for some turkey sandwiches. I slid the Coke we were sharing to my side of the table while sliding a slender box wrapped in cheerful paper over to his side.

"Happy 17th!" I said.

Mickey said curiously, "Is the 17th a Persian holiday of some sort?"

I laughed, "No, silly, we met three months ago on the seventeenth. Happy anniversary! Open it."

He removed the wrapping, a little embarrassed that it hadn't occurred to him that we had been dating for three months. He unfastened the cover, and there, nestled in the slim, black box, was a sleek Betoni pen engraved with his initials along with the inscription: *May you have a very successful writing career.*

Summoning the most eloquent words he could in the moment he scrawled on his café placemat.

> *There exists not the possibility of failure while holding this magnificent pen in my hand. It will imbue me with a profusion of sublime stories, flowing from my mind onto the paper. I will cherish this magical instrument and your inspiration for all time.*

He pushed the placemat across the table for me to read, and then got up and put his arms around me and kissed me.

"Thank you, this is an exceptional gift, and I am deeply touched. I love you."

• • •

My siblings had adjusted to their new lives, and were doing well. Zandra had been hired by a large pharmacy chain and was able to work close to home. Zanna passed all of her dental exams with ease, and was working in the office of another dentist nearby. Thankfully, her medical situation had been resolved with no further complications. Ziggy had taken a position with a medical HMO and had moved an hour's drive from us to Orange County. Maamaan spent the majority of her time with Aunt Sabra and the grandchildren, but was much quieter and introspective since Papa had passed. She still made Shabbat dinner every Friday night for the whole family, insisting that everyone be there or have a very good excuse why not.

Aviva left for college in the fall, and of course Mickey worried about her a great deal, but it gave us the opportunity to spend more time together. Dalia planned to be at her mother's condo for the weekend, so we looked forward to a special movie night at his place. As I walked up the steps to his second floor flat, a stabbing pain from my old injury stopped me in my tracks, taking my breath away. I steadied myself, breathing slowly and deeply, waiting for the pain to subside.

I rang the bell to no answer, but Mickey rarely wore his hearing aids in the apartment. There was no signal light in his office to alert him when someone was at the door, so no one interrupted him while he was writing, so I assumed he was there. I walked the length of his apartment until I reached his office window and waved to get his attention.

The stabbing pain eased off, but I was still hurting, and I did not want it to ruin movie night. Mickey opened the door and, to alleviate my discomfort and to distract him, I did an abbreviated belly dance. I had found this exercise to be effective in reducing pain by visualizing a string attached to my spine with an imaginary puppeteer pulling upwards causing my chest to lift then drop. I added the well-known hip action just to entertain him, and it put a huge grin on Mickey's face.

"Forget movie night! This looks like a lot more fun," he said hopefully.

I was angry with myself for hiding my health issues from Mickey. That old cultural secrecy was raising its ugly head again. As much as I hated it, and tried to rebel against it, my fear of him leaving me was greater. I worried that if I told him, he would visualize our future requiring him to care for an invalid and I was not yet ready to risk that.

He knew about my tinnitus, since he suffered from it too, so that I did not have to conceal. This bothersome incessant ringing, or whooshing noise in the ears affects about one in five people. Thankfully, my hearing aid is designed to help reduce the ringing by fooling my brain with environmental noise. Mickey joked that his tinnitus seemed like a chorus in one ear and a cantor singing in the other. As I became older, mine was more like pots and pans banging in my head — we made quite the *musical* duo.

I took a hydrocodone tablet prescribed by Ziggy and joined Mickey in the kitchen to make popcorn. "What movie did you get?"

"*Forever Young*, a love story, starring Mel Gibson and Jamie Lee Curtis."

"I have to confess that I am a typical woman — a sucker for a good love story," I teased.

"There is nothing typical about you." He kissed me and smiled. "By the way, I'm going to New York in late June to visit some family and friends, and then a week in Connecticut to house sit for my cousin Sarah and take care of her dog. Would you like to come with me?"

"Let me think about it," I said.

We had not yet slept together, so I was conflicted, but his offer was very tempting, and stoked a mental belly dance to an alluring beat that moved through my body.

"Let me know as soon as you can. The earlier I buy the tickets the better fare I can get."

I knew Mickey had to be prudent with his finances. Starting a second career with one daughter in college could be quite a financial strain. He had picked up some work tutoring, and was able to collect disability while getting his writing career off the ground, but living on a fixed income certainly had its challenges.

We cuddled up on the sofa with our popcorn, trying to concentrate on Mel and Jamie Lee, but Mickey's warm breath in my ear and erotic nibbling on my neck made it completely impossible. He had the most enticing brown eyes, and his gentle caresses ignited an intense desire that pulsed a heat through my body.

Forget the movie. We had our own love story unfolding. He kissed me deeply and I surrendered into his firm body. He stood, took me by the hands and tilted his head, gesturing to the bedroom.

"Let's get more comfortable."

Resistance was futile, and nothing could have been further from my mind.

He softly kissed one eye, then the other, sequentially working his way down — my nose, each corner of my mouth, tenderly touching one ear with his tongue, then expertly switching to the other. He leisurely moved down my neck, then carefully opened button after button on my blouse as if each was a tiny piece of fragile crystal. His touch was electrifying; his lips faultlessly arousing. We undressed each other slowly, savoring the passion and luxuriating in the seduction.

Mickey was a generous lover. I had never known such heights of desire. In fact, I had no idea that heights even existed. Finally, I could fully appreciate what a genuine coupling was supposed to be.

As we lay together basking in the afterglow, it occurred to me that of course I would accompany him in June. I switched on the light.

"Something wrong?" Mickey asked.

"Absolutely nothing. I have never been to New York or Connecticut. I think I would really enjoy a nice vacation."

He kissed me passionately, turned off the light, and we held each other gently until sleep took us away.

30

WE LANDED AT THE PHILADELPHIA AIRPORT and rented a car to drive the nine miles to Cherry Hill, where Mickey's cousin, Philip lived in the suburbs with his wife, Jill. He had a very successful business as a podiatrist with several offices in the Philadelphia area.

"Before we get to Philip's place, I want to warn you, so that you are not surprised by his odd behavior. He has not been officially diagnosed, but the family suspects that he suffers from some sort of mental illness. He can be quite unreasonable and erratic at times, and his confrontational style can catch you off guard."

I was curious. "Is he dangerous?"

"He hasn't been that I am aware of, but he can be somewhat aggressive and antagonistic. He can be quite frightening, and I think that is why the family tends to leave him alone so not to push him to violence.

"We grew up together, and I was the best man at his wedding, but I have not seen him in over ten years. We got too busy with life, and when I came east, it was to visit my parents, so we have not stayed in close touch."

Hand-in-hand, we walked up the brick steps to a lovely two-story home and knocked. A dumpy, bald-headed man with dark, Mediterranean features answered the door, but before Mickey could introduce us, Philip angrily said, "What are you doing here?"

"Did you forget we were coming?"

"You're an hour early!" Philip shouted and slammed the door.

Mickey took my hand and said, "Let's grab a bite to eat and we will try again later. We will likely get a different Philip in an hour."

"I am glad you warned me. You were right; that was very weird."

"Wait — it will get weirder," he said as we walked to the car laughing.

After a nice lunch, we returned to Philip's home, and he cordially greeted us as if nothing had happened. He invited us in to the enclosed front porch leading into a magnificent house while he went to find his wife.

"This is such a beautiful house," I said.

"Can you imagine what this place would cost in California?" Mickey asked.

"Over a million," I signed back.

Philip descended the stairs, followed by his demure wife. When they reached the bottom of the staircase, Phillip pointed at us.

"What's all that hand shit about? She deaf?"

"I would like you to meet Zhila, my girlfriend. How astute of you to pick up that she is deaf," Mickey said, mocking Philip. "A lot has happened since we last spoke. I too am deaf and 'that hand shit' helps us understand each other."

Philip paled, and walked off with his arm around Mickey's shoulder, donning a new personality with a genuine air of concern. "Tell me what happened."

Jill and I introduced ourselves as she took me into the sunroom, and we sat overlooking their enormous backyard.

"What happened to Mickey? How did he become deaf?"

"He went to sleep one night and when he awoke the next morning, he could not hear. The doctors suspect it was from a virus, but they do not know for sure."

Tears filled Jill's eyes. "I'm so sorry."

"I'm not!" I snapped. "If not for his deafness, we never would have met." I related the entire account of our meeting, and how I lost my hearing, and then a little about my life in Tehran.

"I'm curious," Jill said, "How do you understand me so well?"

"Lip reading most of the time, although Mickey and I use sign language when we are together, and that makes it easier."

Jill was a lovely person, and invited me on a tour of her home, first leading me to her ten-year-old son, Jadon's room on the second floor.

"Where is he now?" I asked pointing to a plaque inscribed with his name.

"At camp for the next two weeks. Now this," she gestured to another room, "is my art studio with my most recent work." She pointed to a painting of a beautiful old oak tree with a swing hanging from a prominent branch.

"Oh! I love this."

"Thank you. It's one of my favorites, too." We walked up another flight of steps to a remodeled attic. "This is where you and Mickey will stay the night."

"I am sorry, no, we have to be in Voorhees," I checked my watch, "in an hour. Mickey's college friends Leslie and Benny are expecting us."

We finished our tour and then joined Mickey and Philip in the basement-turned-pool room.

I turned to Jill. "Your home is spectacular."

Jill smiled, but her demeanor had changed, and she seemed somewhat disappointed.

Mickey patted Philip on the back and said something I did not get. "Ready to go, Zhila?"

"Jill seemed unhappy that we were leaving," I said as we drove away.

"No big surprise. My cousin can be a real asshole and she probably craves the company of people who are mentally healthy for a change."

"I wonder how he keeps a clientele in his practice with his ornery personality?"

Mickey shrugged. "It's a mystery."

I felt strange to be meeting Mickey's ex-girlfriend, Leslie. He had met her in graduate school in St. Louis at Washington University when he was working on his elementary education degree. They had a relationship for two years before breaking it off when Mickey moved to Los Angeles, but the most intimidating part of meeting her hit me when Mickey mentioned she was a psychotherapist. I instantly thought she would be able to see all my secrets, and I became so anxious I wanted him to turn the car around and go anywhere else.

We drove up to a beautiful split-level home surrounded by trees.

"What a gorgeous setting," I said trying to be calm.

"Wait until you see the inside."

After she opened the front door, a pretty woman with long brown hair and large blue eyes ran into Mickey's arms.

"Zhila, this is Leslie."

Her beauty made me feel awkward and terribly self-conscious. A tall blond man built like a football player appeared in the doorway, and then wrapped Mickey in a big bear hug.

"Good to see you, bro," Mickey said.

The man extended his hand to me. "I'm Benny, Leslie's husband."

Leslie escorted us to the bedroom where we would spend the night. Looking at her watch, she asked, "You guys hungry?"

"Famished," said Mickey.

Benny pulled the car keys from his pocket. "Chinese, right?"

He returned loaded with bags of take-out containers, laying them out on the table. As we dug into the various cartons, Mickey noticed that Leslie was uncharacteristically quiet.

"What's wrong, Les?" he asked.

"Nothing really, I had a rather disturbing encounter today with the doctor in one of your cousin Philip's podiatry offices. I went to have a procedure done on my toe and had a disagreement with the doctor over the bill. I paid what should have been the correct amount and, after arguing with the doctor, I left. Evidently the doctor called Philip to complain, and Philip sent me an email on the doctor's behalf. His over-reaction was clearly that of someone with a mental disorder, so I should not have let it bother me. I printed it out to show Benny because it was so shocking. It's in my purse, I'll show you."

> Leslie, Dr. Gaines explained how you ran off without paying your bill. You are such a bitch. You are not welcome in any of my offices again.

The email went on to deride Leslie with a litany of profanities.

Mickey, annoyed at what Philip had written, asked, "Leslie, would you mind if I borrowed your computer to email Philip about this?"

Trying to keep his temper in check Mickey typed:

> Dear Philip, it was nice seeing you and Jill today after such a long time, but I am concerned. I'm here with Leslie and she showed me a disturbing email from you. How could you behave in such an ill-mannered, despicable, way? You have burned a bridge to a truly wonderful woman. - Cousin Mickey

The next morning at breakfast Leslie handed Mickey a copy of Philip's reply, "It's from Philip, I'm sorry I involved you. I knew I should have just let it go."

> Mickey, you bastard! Taking that slut's side. What kind of family are you? I never want to see your sorry ass around here again.
> - ex-cousin Philip

Looking up after reading Philip's foul response, Leslie gave us her suspected assessment. "Mickey, he needs help. This kind of behavior is usually indicative of someone in a great deal of pain likely fueled by some very deep-seated anger. I'm sorry to say I do not see him getting help on his own."

• • •

After traveling most of the day, we arrived at a beautiful tree-lined neighborhood in West Hartford where Sarah and her husband, Jack, a robotics engineer lived. They were just about to leave to catch their flight to Beijing, so the introductions were short and sweet.

"You must be Zhila. Mickey has told me so much about you," Sarah said.

The scent of her perfume reminded me of springtime in Tehran and I liked her immediately.

"I'm sorry to be in such a rush, but I have left instructions on the kitchen table for anything you might need. You can call, but remember there is a twelve-hour time difference. Make yourselves comfortable, eat, sleep, and do whatever you want."

They kissed Sheba, their nine-year-old beagle goodbye and were off to the airport.

"They seem like very nice people. You are lucky that she is an English teacher; she can help you with your writing, especially since she specializes in writing."

Mickey was working on his book, a story about a violin virtuoso who awoke on his twelfth birthday unable to hear, becoming deaf overnight. I am sure the story incorporates many of the same emotions from his personal experience. It's title, *Between Two Worlds*, was so apropos, reflecting the challenges of being squeezed between deaf and hearing worlds.

"By the way," I said, "one thing I would really love to do while we are here, other than feeding you better so you can shed some of that cute little paunch, is to visit The American School for the Deaf. It is so close by, and I had been reading about its history. Did you know it is the oldest school for the deaf in this country and it has about 4,000 alumni? We must go!"

Since it was early August, ASD was, of course, closed for the summer break, but we were able to stroll the grounds and enjoy its lush green lawns and modern buildings, feeling as if we were now included in its history.

After a wonderful week in Hartford, we woke early, catching the morning train to New York City. Mickey went to great lengths to make it an exceptional vacation, showing me all the famous places for which the city was known: Times Square, the Guggenheim Museum, and Liberty Island to see the iconic Statue of Liberty. While on the boat, Mickey took photos of the New York skyline with the famous World Trade Center skyscrapers delineated among the hodgepodge of buildings. Who would ever have imagined the horror that lay ahead for the unsuspecting people of New York and the colossal Twin Towers? In a short month, America would suffer an unspeakable disaster, leaving them reeling for years, never to be the same again.

31

SIX MONTHS AFTER THE MONSTROUS ATTACKS on our nation, we continued to struggle to make sense of this insanity. The country shared a collective trauma worsened by the repeated exposure to TV footage of the incursion. Militant Islamic extremists sequentially crashed two hijacked passenger planes through the World Trade Center Towers in New York City, then attacked the center of our military, the Pentagon. The fourth suicide mission to destroy the White House was heroically foiled by passengers who overwhelmed the terrorists and intentionally downed the plane in a Pennsylvania field, saving the seat of our stability as a nation.

The madness of this inhumanity, and the loss of almost 3,000 souls, was impossible to sort out or understand, turning our nation's ability to reason on its head. We were jittery and uneasy, not knowing what might happen next, permeated by a mix of emotions we could not name. We desperately clung to anything normal. To cope, Mickey and I spent as much time as possible in the sanctity of nature away from the headlines and a world gone mad. Our destination, on a beautiful summer day, was the hiking trails of the Tree People Estates in the Santa Monica Mountains. This environmental organization had been established in the early 1970s with a mission to inspire Angelinos to plant trees and learn ways to use water efficiently in this Mediterranean climate.

I should have known better than to start a conversation as Mickey sped up the mountain road, but my curiosity got the best of me and before I thought it through.

"Whatever happened with your cousin Philip?"

"I got an email from Jill the other day. She has filed for divorce and she and Jadon have moved into their own place. Luckily, Philip's brother was able to encourage him to get therapy, although I don't know if he actually followed through with it, but maybe he did, because now he is dating, if you can imagine that."

It was hard for me to concentrate when Mickey signed and drove at the same time; it made me especially nervous when he took both hands off the wheel to emphasize a point. Mulholland was a very winding highway and, as he snaked around a particularly tight turn, he lost control of the car and we skidded across the lane.

With the deftness of a racecar driver, Mickey was pleased with his miraculous recovery and continued down the twisting road.

"PULL OVER!" I demanded.

I sat motionless until I could stop shaking and my heart stopped pounding.

"That does it! I will not ride with you if you sign while you are driving. It is too dangerous. You scared me half to death."

Mickey nodded trying to calm me. "I know, I know, you are right. From now on, I promise if the car is moving, we will rely on lip-reading only or we will pull over."

"Agreed."

• • •

The Tree People had built a cobbled pathway that we followed to a stairway leading to a dirt path. "My dog Kelly loved coming here."

Mickey had never mentioned his dog before, so I asked, "What kind of dog was Kelly?"

"L-A-B," he finger-spelled, "with beautiful black fur. She was a great dog."

As we sat on a bench overlooking the valley, Mickey's mood turned inward, so I asked, "What happened to Kelly?"

Mickey's foot casually swept at the leaves scattered on the ground around the bench. "A few years ago, I gave her to a friend, because I had to move. I was not able to manage the balloon payment due on my condo, so I sold it. The place I found would not allow pets, and the condo sold quickly, so I had to move in a hurry."

We passed hikers with their dogs on the trail, and I could see in Mickey's eyes how much he missed his dog.

"That's so sad," I said.

"I miss her a lot, but Kelly has a great home, and my daughters were able to switch to better schools, and the rent was more affordable. In retrospect, it was all for the best."

A couple walking toward us waved at Mickey. The woman was tall and elegant; the white-haired, bearded man looked like he could be her father.

"That is Rebecca, my ex-wife and her husband, Shmuel."

Rebecca hurried up to Mickey and kissed both his cheeks, and said something to him in Hebrew. I knew a little Hebrew, but never mastered the ability to lip-read it.

Mickey made the introductions, and Rebecca kissed my cheeks too, and held both my hands.

While looking at me, she said to Mickey, "She is absolutely lovely, just as you described."

Rebecca was very kind and made a point to include me in the conversation, unlike many hearing people I had met.

Shmuel checked his watch, "We would love to stay and chat, but we have a wedding this evening and must get going." He gestured to his shorts and t-shirt. "We just came for a bit of exercise."

"Nice to meet you, Zhila. I hope to see you at Dalia's *bat mitzvah*."

As they walked away, I said, "Rebecca is gorgeous. Why did you divorce?" I had hinted at this subject on previous occasions, but Mickey always managed to avoid talking about it.

"Shmuel has two daughters and our girls have known each other all their lives. We decided to raise our kids in a peaceful and loving environment, so we are nice to each other. Does that bother you?"

He had taken a slight defensive posture to my question, which confirmed that this was indeed a sensitive area.

"On the contrary, it is refreshing to witness such civility. I have no doubt that is why you have two lovely, well-adjusted daughters, but you did not answer my question."

Mickey let out a distressed puff of air and led me over to a bench and we sat down. "It's complicated."

"Divorce is always complicated," I said knowingly.

"Rebecca secretly ran up over $50,000 in debt, all in my name. I could no longer trust her, so one night, while she was asleep, I cut up all her credit cards."

"Oh, my God! What did she do?"

"She found the credit card pieces on the kitchen counter the next morning and knew she had been caught. Instead of confessing or even showing a willingness to discuss it, she had a tantrum and stopped speaking to me. Anyone, much less a wife who would keep secrets of that magnitude, is not capable of creating a true relationship, only self-gratification.

"But the most decisive reason was that she stopped respecting me, which you could also translate to she stopped loving me. This story will clearly demonstrate the death of our marriage:

"There was an earthquake that damaged my bedroom closet. I had it rebuilt and, a week after the work was finished, I came home to find Rebecca's clothes hanging in my new closet and my clothes laid out on the bed. I was confused and furious at the same time and asked her, as calmly as I could, why her clothes were hanging in my closet." After a quiet pause, he said, "You will never believe her answer."

I was hanging on every incredulous word, "What?"

"*That closet is too good for you.* Even after all this time, it still stings to recall those words."

My heart ached for him. He was the kindest man I had ever known. Rebecca had given me the impression that she was so caring; it just did not add up. How could a decent person intentionally say such hurtful things to someone she professed to love, unless she harbored a secret hated? I put my arms around him and held him close. I could feel the sorrow in his body and finally understood why he had been reluctant to talk about it. But, now knowing his strong feelings about secrecy, I was even more scared to tell him the things I had been withholding.

We walked silently down the path when suddenly up ahead a deer appeared. We stood frozen watching each other until something spooked this beautiful creature and it moved into the woods. It was a special Mother Nature moment that you do not often experience living in the city and it significantly changed the mood.

"Zhila, we've been together nearly three years ..." Unexpectedly, he dropped to one knee, took a small, white box out of his pocket, opened it, and said, "I'm ready for the next step and I hope you are too? Will you marry me?"

I never saw this coming, and was caught completely off-balance, stammering and babbling, making no sense at all. I was not prepared, and could not look Mickey in the eye. All I could manage to say that made any sense was the cliché, non-committal, "I have to think about it." I felt like the lowest person on earth after just having heard the heart-wrenching story of his divorce.

The disappointment on Mickey's face tore at my heart. His hands were trembling as he snapped the lid closed on the ring box and tried to contain his emotions.

"I will interpret that as a 'NO'. I realize we have never talked about it, but I assumed after three years, you would have expected this, and I wanted to surprise you. I guess this was a stupid thing to do."

Ashamed, I shook my head, "No, you have been wonderful, and I love you deeply, I ..."

"What?" Mickey pleaded.

"I have health issues that I have kept from you, and I was afraid if I told you, you would leave me and then, by not telling you, it became more difficult to tell you. I did not want you to think that you would be stuck marrying an invalid that you would have to care for. My medical expenses are covered under government plans and, if we married, I would lose that and I could never put the responsibility of my medical expenses on you. I am a coward, I know, and this secrecy has been crushing me, but facing the possibilities was worse."

The admission came tumbling out all in one long breath, but the relief after having withheld it for three years brought a tremendous release.

"What medical problems do you have?"

"Well obviously my hearing and tinnitus, but the worst condition that I suffer from is chronic back pain from a car accident I had as a teen."

I took a deep breath to reveal the one condition I would barely even admit to myself. "I also suffer from occasional depression and need my privacy. It is difficult for people to understand if they have never experienced it, but I cannot be around people when I have an episode, and I would not have the privacy necessary to deal with it if we married and lived together."

Mickey listened thoughtfully. "This actually helps clarify some things, but going forward you must be honest with me. We can continue our relationship as is under one condition: I insist we be engaged. I want to show everyone my commitment to you and to our relationship."

I smiled through my tears and said, "You cannot imagine the amount of relief I feel. These are the happy tears of liberation."

"One last thing," Mickey said sheepishly, "Do you like the ring?"

I was reluctant to appear inconsiderate, but he wanted honesty. I shook my head, "It is very nice, but it is not a style that matches my affection for you."

"I understand, it did feel a bit wrong picking it out without you, so they told me I could exchange it, if necessary, for one of your preference."

"They are very wise!" I signed, "I have one condition too. Since a committed relationship requires two, we must get a ring for you also."

32

A BAR MITZVAH is an ancient coming-of-age ritual in the life of a Jewish boy, a rite of passage recognizing adulthood. It marks their commitment and responsibility as a member of the Jewish People. Not until modern times, among contemporary Jews, was the practice expanded to include girls. Slowly over decades, as the role of women changed, girls were finally allowed to participate in this practice with a *bat mitzvah*. These are cherished traditions within the Jewish community, and Mickey's daughters, Dalia and Aviva, dedicated four years to their Jewish studies and Hebrew school in preparation to become sanctioned members of their community.

Mickey did not want to miss a second of Dalia's *bat mitzvah*, so he hired a sign language interpreter, even though most of the service was conducted in Hebrew. Eighty-five of Dalia's friends and family gathered at the hotel to affirm this singular event.

Rebecca greeted us after the service with warm hugs. "It is a beautiful sadness that our last baby is all grown up. I get upset with myself when I think I almost denied my daughters this significant milestone. In Israel, when I was growing up, it was not acceptable for girls to have a *bat mitzvah*. It was not done; only boys were allowed a ceremony."

"It was the same for me growing up in Iran. I just had a party when I turned thirteen," I said.

"Aviva came home from Hebrew school one day very excited about planning her *bat mitzvah* and I immediately squashed her enthusiasm, refusing to allow it. I told her, 'No! My daughter will not read from Torah. I did not, my mother did not, and you will not either! Your grandfather would never approve.'"

"How did Mickey react to that?"

Rebecca looked at Mickey and smiled. "He wisely suggested we attend a *bat mitzvah* to see what it was like. Surprisingly, the ceremony was really touching, but at the same time, it punctured years of rationale I had accepted. It stirred up a multi-layered sorrow of my own that I had to face, but I realized I could partially remedy it through my girls." She kissed Mickey and said, "I am grateful that Mickey allowed me to find my way in his classic, tactful style."

While everyone was dancing, Mickey and I sat down at an empty table to enjoy the tremendous spread of food. The music was so loud we removed our hearing aids for a break from the noise. "I am curious," I signed, "how did Rebecca and Shmuel meet?"

"Shmuel and his wife, Rita, were our best friends."

Mickey paused to let the subtlety of his statement sink in. I laid down my fork, preparing for what I suspected was going to be another heartbreaking story in the life of Mickey Daniels. I looked at him expectantly, signaling I was ready for the rest of the story.

"Rebecca missed Israel terribly; she was lonely and wanted to meet other Israelis. I discovered an Israeli couple with an infant daughter who lived in our condo complex — in fact, just down the hall. I knocked on their door and introduced myself and told them about Rebecca, and our friendship began. Unfortunately for Rita and me, Shmuel and Rebecca later decided to become even closer, consummating their friendship with an affair."

I swallowed a bite of salad to hide my shock, "But you still speak to him?"

"Yes, I did not want our children to grow up feeling as if they had to choose sides. Animosity does not make a good environment for children."

"I could never be that understanding."

"Yes, you could. I swallowed my pride for my girls. When you have children, you make decisions based on what is best for them. You do not have the luxury of indulging in your own pettiness."

"The more I learn about you just keeps confirming why I fell in love with you. You have an innate decency and good heart that is rare. I am amazed at how you can rise above your emotions for the greater good." With a bit of humility, I admitted, "I have become a better person and like myself more since being with you."

Dalia flashed the lights to get our attention and then announced the candle lighting ceremony was about to begin. Mickey was so proud looking at her: grown up and beautiful, standing graciously before the crowd.

With microphone in hand, she called up thirteen significant people in her life, one-by-one, each having the honor to light one of the 14 candles arranged in the candelabra. Taking her time, making sure that each person individually grasped the depth of her gratitude, she offered her heartfelt thank-you for her upbringing and good fortune, praising each for the important role they had played.

"Daddy — You are my inspiration, my anchor, and guide. Thank you for everything you have done for me. I love you so much and I am so grateful and so lucky." Then she kissed him gently on the cheek, trying to keep her composure.

She finally reached the fourteenth candle, looked over at me and signed, "Candle fourteen, to me, is magical. I have added it to the traditional thirteen for a very important person. Zhila, please come up."

Not certain that I had understood her correctly, I pointed at myself as if to say, *You mean me?* She nodded her head. gesturing for me to come forward. Self-consciously, I stood and approached the flickering candelabra.

Dalia simultaneously signed and spoke, "Magically, you have made my father very happy and have been a marvelous mentor and friend to me. I love you, Zhila."

I lit my candle, trying to hold back a flood of tears. After Dalia kissed my cheek, I hurried back to my seat. wishing I had brought tissue and worn waterproof mascara.

• • •

We celebrated the New Year in Hawaii on the beautiful garden island of Kauai with my dear friend Goli and her husband. She and I chattered endlessly in Farsi and giggled like schoolgirls, painfully boring the men with our syrupy nostalgia and stories, even though they had no idea what we were talking about.

Goli took us to the charming resort where she worked, showing us where the cruise ships anchored in the bay.

"I must go to work," she said. "But I have made a list with directions to the places you must see while you are on the island."

We parked our rental car at the Waimea Canyon Lookout and strolled hand-in-hand to the canyon's edge, timidly looking down 3,000 feet to the lush greenery below.

"Did you know that the marriage ceremony of the ancient Hawaiians was simply an agreement to cohabitate?" Mickey asked.

"I did not know that, my sweet, brilliant history teacher," I teased.

Mickey took my hands in his, slowly pledging, "Zhila, I do not need to stand under a wedding canopy before family and friends to confirm my love and commitment to you. Healthy and vibrant, ailing or depressed, it matters not; I will always love and support you."

Captured in this powerfully poignant moment, we looked out over the chasm to behold a vivid rainbow forming an arch over the gorge. It was unmistakable — our ancient Kauai union had been blessed by God.

33

WHEN THE STUDENTS THAT MICKEY TUTORED went on summer break, he took advantage of the timing and planned his vacation to coincide. This year, we made plans to stay at a timeshare in Lake Tahoe, after making a couple of stops along the way. We were both really excited to have some more quality Mother Nature time.

Mickey's brother and his wife, Phyllis, lived in a small community in the southern Sierra Nevada Mountains, a three-hour drive from Los Angeles. He was recovering from a recent cancer surgery, and Mickey felt he better check in on him and see what his future with this diagnosis might be.

Larry was reclining on the sofa munching on pretzels when we arrived. The TV was blaring loudly as he spoke to us, we could not understand anything he said. Mickey pointed to the TV and then pointed to his ears shaking his head and Phyllis quickly picked up the remote to turn it down.

"I'm so sorry," she apologized, "He can be so annoying. Maybe he is losing his hearing, too; he always has that damned volume so loud!"

We let out a sigh of relief as the raucous noise faded into the background.

"Sorry to barge in so last minute, but we are on our way to Tahoe and wanted to check in on you. How are you feeling?"

Larry said, "Not bad for only a week post-surgery. They tell me they caught it early, so I should make a full recovery. I have to follow up with my doc occasionally to make sure, but that is no big deal. You should see your doctor and get your colon checked out too. You never know."

Mickey promised he would take his brother's advice to heart, and we hit the road for our next stop, Virginia City. Mickey was fascinated by the supernatural, especially ghosts, so he had made reservations at The International Hotel, which was rumored to be haunted. I had no fondness for the spooky stuff, but this area of the country had an extensive geological history that I was eager to probe.

As we checked in to the hotel, we coincidentally met a thirty-something deaf woman who was staying at the hotel with her mother and young son.

"I'm Leslie," she signed. "Nice to meet other deafies. That doesn't happen often when I'm traveling. You know this hotel is haunted, right?"

Mickey introduced us and said, "I had heard it was haunted, but didn't know if it was true. Have you actually seen a ghost in the hotel?"

"No," she signed, "but last night the lights flashed on and off in my room. And my mother said she heard noises."

She shared Mickey's enthusiasm for the paranormal and signed very rapidly, so I had a hard time following her. Mickey filled in the gaps for me later, confirming there was a hotel plaque that described several murders and suicides in its history, and they believed these disembodied spirits stuck around after they died.

Leslie changed the subject and asked, "Have you been to the Ponderosa Saloon yet?

I said, "No, not yet. We just got here."

"It isn't haunted, but it's really a neat place. There is a mine at the rear of the saloon that used to be a working mine during the gold rush days, but now it is only a tourist attraction, and they have a tour."

We had lunch at the saloon and got a discount on the tour that lasted less than a half hour. It featured a display of mining equipment and tools, its history, and an explanation of how they extracted the gold. I found the geology so interesting and was able to lip-read our tour guide and fill in the gaps that Mickey missed.

We were exhausted after a long day and fell asleep as soon as our heads hit the luxurious hotel pillows. After a refreshing night's sleep, I awoke and turned over to gently wake Mickey, but he was already up. I looked at the clock: strange; Mickey rarely gets up this early. Through the curtains, I saw his silhouette on the balcony and opened the sliding door. There stood Mickey with his back to me, looking out over Virginia City's main street sipping on a bottle of water. I gently kissed him on the back of the neck, scaring him so badly his arms flew into the air throwing his bottle over the balcony.

He turned tapping his hand against his heart, "Geez, you nearly gave me a heart attack!"

"Sorry, I was trying to be romantic. I guess you are not wearing your hearing aids. Why are you up so early? This is vacation, remember?"

"I couldn't sleep. I had a visitor in the middle of the night, and I cannot stop thinking about it."

I teased him, not realizing he was serious. "Really? Did Leslie's ghost stories worm into your mind, impelling you to dream about disembodied spirits?"

He shook his head. "No, seriously, I jolted awake and saw a pinprick of light on the wall opposite our bed. The pinprick got larger as it crept up the wall, across the ceiling and then began to morph into a gaunt face with translucent skin."

"Stop! You are scaring me. Honestly, you saw that?"

"Yes, I swear! It appeared to be a woman with long, braided, messy hair that looked like wild snakes growing out of her head. She pointed to a pendant around her neck with a purple stone."

My face drained of color and I gasped, "My God! You just described my grandmother, Gerty! She had very long braids that she wound around the top of her head and she always wore a purple pendant."

"Now you are scaring me!" Mickey laughed nervously, "Your grandmother's face crept down the wall behind our bed and when I asked who she was she stuck her tongue out at me and disappeared."

"Oh my God! This is just too creepy! My grandmother was a very peculiar woman. When we were young, she would make strange faces and stick her tongue out at us for no apparent reason."

Mickey said, "Well, it really freaked me out, and, after she disappeared, I couldn't sleep. Maybe she was somehow on your mind on this trip, and you conjured her up. This is too weird even for me. I would rather not stay a second night. Do you mind if we leave for Tahoe after breakfast?"

The beautiful drive to Tahoe calmed our nerves, and we had a nice alpine lunch overlooking the lake, after which we went our separate ways. Mickey wanted to go to the casino to gamble, which I found to be a ridiculous wasteful vice. Why would anyone just throw away hard-earned money for fun? He dropped me off to go shopping at the aptly named, Heavenly Village, promising to pick me up in a couple hours.

I bought some souvenirs, and found The Old Timey Photo Shoppe, and decided to spend some money for a keepsake, transporting me back in time to the Old West. I selected the Annie Oakley costume — a character that represented everything I was not. I dressed in a buckskin outfit with wide-brimmed hat, and a long rifle slung over my shoulder.

The photographer advised, "Don't smile, now give me an *'I will kick your butt' face*," and snapped my picture. "If anyone asks, tell them you are a famous nineteenth century American sharpshooter."

I got carried away in my fantasy world and realized I was five minutes late to meet Mickey. I rushed down the street to the jewelry store where we had agreed to meet, but he had not arrived yet either. I was relieved I had not kept him waiting, and sat on a bench in front of the store admiring my Annie Oakley picture and waited.

After thirty minutes, I began to worry. Maybe he had an accident, or got mugged leaving the casino, or the car broke down, or, or, or … I allowed myself to get carried away dreaming up the worst possible scenarios that could have happened. Staring down at my photo, Annie Oakley did not seem to offer any courage, although I really did want to kick his butt. Finally, fifteen very long minutes later, my wayward gambler pulled up, grinning like the Cheshire cat.

I barely gave him a chance to get out of the car before I started screaming at him scaring away the Cheshire smile. "Do you realize you have left me sitting here for forty-five minutes, worried sick, thinking you must be dead. I am furious! Where have you been? And it better be a damn good excuse."

"Well, I was winning at Blackjack and couldn't stop in the middle of a hot streak and sure enough I was right because I won $2,000. Isn't that great!" He paused for a minute, studying my face to see if that helped his cause.

"Great?? You think that is Great! That is NOT great and is NOT an excuse! In fact, some people would say you have a gambling problem. Do you think $2000 makes this alright?"

"If I had a gambling problem, which I do not, I would have stayed until I lost the $2000, thinking I could win more. But I knew when to quit — no problem. I will admit it was lousy of me to keep you waiting and worrying, and I am very sorry.

"I think we can solve this by doing something we should have done long ago. Just hear me out — we can purchase a cell phone for you, like mine, so we can text each other. Don't you think it is time, Zhila? This technology is vital; every deaf person should have one. I promise it will make life so much easier for us both."

"I will admit, it is time, but I cannot switch my emotions off just like that, especially when I am this infuriated. Nor can you buy me off so easily with gambling money. Maybe by the time we drive to the Apple Store, I will be finished brooding," I said only half-joking.

After dinner, Mickey worked on the short story he was writing, while I played with my new toy. I immediately taught myself how to send text messages. The first one went to Zanna, and I was shocked at how quickly her reply came back accompanied by a smiley face:

ABT TME! WLCME TO THE MODRN WRLD!!!

After I figured out the code, I felt a little foolish that I had allowed my apprehension to get the best of me and put this off for so long.

34

MONTHS LATER, Dr. Zimmerman got right to the point. "Zhila I realize you know this already, but I cannot emphasize it enough. A cochlear implant requires surgery, carrying all the risks of surgery. A hearing aid is designed to increase the volume of sound, but the CI is a very different type of technology that sends sound waves to the brain to interpret. The big question is: are you patient enough to train your brain to translate the signals?

"Many people have the impression that getting a CI will completely restore their hearing after it is implanted. I want to make sure you thoroughly understand this is not like a kidney or heart transplant, where you receive an organic replacement. The CI is a mechanical tool that does not replace a normal ear. It will require a great deal of training on your part to be successful. You will have to be dedicated in your efforts to train your brain to interpret the electronic signals it receives. It is a time-consuming process, and I have to make sure that all my patients understand that it is not easy. I have one last admonition: recognizing speech is the hardest part of the CI to master, so do not expect that to happen until well into the process. I realize I have probably overwhelmed you with an extreme amount of information. Do you have any questions for me now?"

"Dr. Zimmerman, I have waited my entire life for this. I assure you that I am one hundred percent ready to do everything required to make this work."

"I understand that, but let's make sure that the enthusiasm you feel now does not cloud the reality of what it is like to live with this device."

House Ear Institute in Los Angeles was the leading facility in the country for hearing and ear research and education. I received counseling and training there before and after the surgery. Over the better part of a year, my audiologist, Tracy, programmed, reprogrammed, and adjusted my CI, teaching me all the communication techniques necessary to get the most benefit from it. It was very similar to the experience of the man who spoke about it at my first SHHH meeting years earlier.

The biggest advantage was, to my delight, that I could hear classical symphonies, but, despite months of therapy, I was profoundly disappointed that I could not hear voices as well as I had expected, and I began to lose hope.

I was so angry with myself for not having more patience, and not being able to find joy in the benefit I did get. I was not able to stop myself from focusing on the negatives despite Dr. Zimmerman's warnings. I subconsciously hoped that I would be that one person whose hearing would be restored. My disappointment intensified my anger with myself, and I got trapped in a vicious circle, spiraling into depression.

Other health problems that can precipitate from this kind of gloom struck me and I took to my bed. For days, I slept to avoid the hopelessness and apathy that washed over me. I shunned everyone — even Mickey, until the day he showed up to save me from myself.

He let himself into the apartment and came into the bedroom, opening the shades and windows to wake me up and let some fresh air and light into the room.

Against all my protests and whining, he said, "I will wait in the living room while you dress."

He was being very mysterious, but his intense, confident demeanor piqued my curiosity enough that I did as he asked. It took some time to get myself presentable — at least I could still feel shame not wanting him to see me in this disgusting condition.

I sauntered reticently into the living room to see him playing with a tiny brown and white, long-haired fur ball. He was a green-eyed beauty, and it was love at first sight.

"He is a Maine Coon kitten, and they told me at the shelter, if you were not happy with him, you could bring him back and choose a different one — just like your engagement ring."

"He is perfect and so are you," I said, breaking into sobs that turned into that ugly cry that no one wants to hear, but Mickey embraced me, encouraging me to let it all out.

I lost all track of time until I felt my new little fur ball trying to snuggle up with us, which made me smile, and miraculously I started to feel a little hungry.

Mickey's quiet brilliance always left me awed. My creative, sensitive, genius took the chance that this little kitten would help pull me out of my prison. I was always so stunned at the level of caring and patience he possessed, and was indebted to him for being a constant reminder of all things bright and beautiful.

My little Yogi was the exact prescription that I needed to get out of my head and stop thinking so much — which made it possible to look at life with more gratitude. I discovered with my implant I could hear Yogi mew! That was a blessing. I was forever texting Mickey, sharing his silly exploits, and leaning on him for guidance since I had never owned a pet before.

"Yogi ran away!"

"Don't worry, he'll be back."

"Yogi brought home a dead mouse. It is so gross!"

"It's a gift, he loves you."

"Yogi jumped up on the table and licked the dressing off my salad."

"He will be fine, it's healthy dressing."

"He won't stop screaming to go out."

"It's time to see the vet."

Mickey and Yogi were my healers and they brought me joy.

35

THE ENTIRE FAMILY USED TO GATHER every Friday night without fail for our Shabbat meal at Maamaan's, but, as life changed for my siblings, her expansive dinner table was no longer required. Our tradition had dwindled to only five: Maamaan, Zandra, Chava, Mickey, and I — a more subdued ritual. The only times we were able to bring all fourteen of us together now was for the most important holidays. I missed them terribly and obsessed about their happiness.

Zandra was the most observant in the family, and was very strict about devoting the Sabbath to prayer and rest. After all these years, she had not divorced her despicable husband. He still lived in Tehran, and she had no desire to have contact with him, and never mentioned divorcing him — which gave the impression that she had no interest in another relationship.

My niece, Chava, followed her mother's fervent Orthodox practice, although she had not yet married. She was a beautiful and bright woman, with many admirers and offers of marriage, but no one yet aroused her enough to accept. She was not willing to settle just for the sake of satisfying accepted conventions, but now almost thirty, she began to worry that her future as a wife and mother was slipping away.

Zanna and Lassi tended to move a lot, ostensibly to accommodate his health. First, they relocated to the ocean and, when that failed, they tried the desert, hoping for better results. I maintained that this was Lassi's covert attempt to separate Zanna from family. How can you argue with health complications? It is the perfect trap: then he could punish her with impunity for making him move to the states. Now living three hours away, she was completely vulnerable and isolated, having to deal with a difficult husband alone. Lassi had refused to adapt to life here, and claimed he could not work or do much of anything, so Zanna had to carry the full financial and emotional burden.

I complained often to Mickey about my family's troubles. He tried to sympathize, but also pointed out that I was taking on their problems as my own.

"It is very easy to see the solutions to other people's problems, but you cannot live for them or force your viewpoint. You can only listen and empathize because they will, by nature, always resist any attempt for others to solve their problems. If you truly want to help them then be a good listener and ask meaningful questions that will lead them to their own solutions."

Mickey practiced his philosophy, crafting the exact right questions leading me to examine my life, and compelling me to admit to myself that I obsessed over my sibling's problems to avoid my own.

This introspective path led first to my job. The Jewish Home had informed me that I would have to pursue my R.N. degree if I wanted to continue working there. My position was being phased out to satisfy new requirements. The idea of going back to school to earn another degree felt overwhelming. Most likely, I would not be accepted into a nursing program because of my age, the expense was more than I could handle, and the time required would consume my life. After working at the Jewish Home for almost twenty years, I was settled and comfortable, so when they informed me that my position was being eliminated, my reaction was utter panic. To regain my stability, I simply disregarded the entire situation and continued to complain.

"Zhila," Mickey counseled. "Happiness comes from within. Eighteen years ago, I was miserable, but no amount of complaining made me happy. Eventually my friends tired of listening to me — especially when I did nothing to fix it so that I could move forward. I finally realized, if I didn't face the obstacles blocking me, I would be stuck forever. I did face it and did solve it, divorcing my wife and letting the painful memories go. Then miraculously I met you, so you see there is power in facing things and letting go."

Mickey's wise counsel helped pull me out of the boring, sniveling character I had become, I hated myself. Where did he find this endless repository of wisdom and patience?

I realized that my panic over being terminated had completely closed off my ability to consider solutions. Slowly, I began to see life through a more positive lens and, in a moment of clarity, I was hit with the simplicity that, with my years of experience, I could just go back to work for private agencies.

• • •

I had been having occasional abdominal pains over several years, but they always seemed to subside, so I did not pay them much attention nor did I tell anyone. But each time the pain hit, I noticed it was a little more severe.

I was not feeling very well and went to bed early while Mickey stayed up to read. Two hours later, excruciating pain woke me; but this time there was also blood, leaving no doubt this could not be ignored any longer. Blood is a forceful catalyst for action.

Mickey tried to hide his grave concern, but I could see he was very upset. He drove me the two short miles to the emergency room where they did routine tests, gave me pain medication, and referred me for a colonoscopy.

I called Ziggy the next day and he made arrangements to have the procedure done at UCLA within the week. There are not many things that can produce as much anxiety as a hospital, so it was an exceptional blessing to be driven by my personal doctor and have him hold my hand through the trauma of hospital tests. They provided me a nurse who could sign and, with Ziggy running interference and leading the way through the maze of halls and chaos, I relaxed. I wondered how people without these intimate connections made it through without having a breakdown.

The procedure was relatively short, but the anesthesia knocked me out for about three hours. While I slept, the doctor and Ziggy discussed the test results and a medical plan, while agreeing it was best for the news to come from Ziggy. My life had been a string of one catastrophe after another, so I was predisposed to expect disaster. This was why the awful news did not turn my world upside down. All I could think about was: How am I going to tell my sweet, sensitive Mickey?

Ziggy and I came into the apartment, where Mickey was nervously waiting, the worry and agitation thick in the room.

"Mickey, please sit down," Ziggy said solemnly. "There is no easy way to tell you this, Zhila has stage four colon cancer. Stage four is very serious, and her treatment must start immediately."

After speaking the reality out loud the three of us huddled together and sobbed. The two men I loved most in the world were here with me as we absorbed the truth of the dreadful news. I was so blessed to have such unconditional love.

"What happens next?" Mickey asked, his body wracked in the aftermath of sobbing grief.

"Next week, Zhila will see an oncologist at City of Hope; this is their specialty. It is about a forty-five-minute drive from Sherman Oaks ..."

"What if I don't want treatment?" I interrupted. "I have seen my patients suffer terribly from chemo. They lose their hair. They feel hopeless and sick all the time, and often they die anyway."

"Zhila, what would I do without you?" Mickey pleaded in between sobs. "Ziggy told us this is serious, and you could die without treatment. You are my anchor and, if you are gone, I would be lost. We must try. Please don't make me live without you!"

In the early morning rush hour traffic, Mickey drove me the forty-five minutes to City of Hope where Ziggy was to meet us. *Hope* was all we had, but, despite that, the spring of 2010 launched the most difficult stage of my life.

36

I*T'S NOT THE BEST DAYS, but the worst, that forge true love.* Mickey offered that wise aphorism to help us persevere through the lengthy and vicious chemo treatments. Envision a red-hot piece of metal being forcibly pounded into something newly unique and you can comprehend the truth in that statement.

The stress from this ordeal is equally hard on your partner who witnesses the daily pounding their loved one suffers from this poison. The quote by German philosopher, Friedrich Nietzsche: "That which does not kill us, makes us stronger" summarized my partnership with this concoction of so-called life-saving drugs. Nietzsche was an extreme pessimist and radical skeptic who condemned existence — chemotherapy undeniably bullies one into subscribing to his philosophy.

The dangling carrot at the end of months of debilitating therapy was Mickey's promise of a Carnival Cruise to the Mexican Riviera. I visualized this glorious ocean voyage each time I cleansed chemo puke from my mouth.

City of Hope was a beautiful 110-acre campus with an exquisite fountain at its entrance depicting their theme of hope. Spraying water rained down from a spire at its center, topped by a sculpture of parents dancing while they lifted a baby to the sky.

"Well, it is hopeful," Mickey signed.

This was our inaugural appointment to meet my doctors and to learn what to expect over the next several months.

Dr. Chung, my oncologist, began by reassuring me, "This is a substantial facility with vast resources. We collaborate with an excellent team of doctors, nurses, scientists, and an extensive support staff fighting with you and your family to survive this crisis.

"Zhila, your test results show that, in addition to cancer cells in the colon, you have a small tumor in the liver that appears to be operable. Our course of treatment includes four months of chemotherapy, first to shrink the tumor and kill the cancer cells. If we are not satisfied with those results, we will then add radiation therapy. Once we are satisfied, we will schedule two separate surgeries: the first to remove any remaining cancer cells in the colon, and the second to remove the liver tumor.

"Next week, we will implant a tiny pump into your right arm to administer your chemo, then every week you will return for another round, requiring five hours each. We will repeat that for five weeks and then you will have a one-week break to regain some stamina. The entire process will be finished in four months, and then hopefully we will be able to schedule the first surgery sometime in August.

"I realize this is a tremendous amount of information to take in, but please try not to worry too much. We have been treating patients for almost 100 years, so have had the luxury of refining our methods for a long time. Our expert staff is at your disposal to assist and to answer any question you have. In fact, the next person you will meet is your counselor who you will liaise with throughout your treatment. She is a specialist, trained in side effects and remedies and has tremendous experience to prepare you for everything to come. If you are ready, I will introduce you to her now."

While we waited to meet her, Mickey apologized, "I am so sorry you have to go through all this, especially if you are doing it mostly for me."

His eyes filled with tears, and I squeezed his hand. "We will get through this. I can be tough when I have to be."

My counselor gave me the list of possible side effects — muscle and joint pain, nausea and vomiting, fatigue, weakness, numbness, nerve-damage — a long list, along with remedies. Intellectually, it terrified me, but her detailed explanations did not come close to matching the reality of the misery. The one unexpected ray of sunshine in this nightmare was that the chemo mysteriously eliminated my chronic back pain.

As the treatments continued, I got progressively sicker, hardly able to get out of bed, and assaulted by constant waves of nausea. The strength in my body had been zapped, my legs so weak they could barely support my weight. Mickey was so committed and steadfast in his care despite my dramatic demands, barking orders at him to get me this or get me that or leave me alone to die. I was a dreadful patient, but his devotion got me through, and I prayed: God, when Mickey gets to heaven, please reward him generously for loving me through this and enduring my abuse.

• • •

Mickey sped down the freeway, south to San Diego to catch the cruise ship at B Street Pier. His daughters, Aviva and Dalia, assured us we had plenty of time and they were hungry, so we foolishly stopped for lunch. As we merged back onto the freeway, traffic came to an immediate stand still. Our hearts sank as the 3:00 p.m. departure time loomed, wearing away at our enthusiasm. Then miraculously, traffic slowly started inching forward. We worked our way around the culprit, passing a twisted mass of metal that, according to Dalia, was once a nine-million-dollar Lamborghini. I was very curious how she knew that, but that was a conversation for another time; we had only 15 minutes to make up 30 miles.

Mickey succeeded at the impossible pulling into the parking lot with no time to spare. "Aviva, you hurry ahead and locate the purser. Tell him we are bringing the luggage and will be there very soon. Beg him if you have to not to leave without us."

Yosie Bock, a tall, curly haired purser, calmly smiled at Aviva, "No worries, we'll get you on board in plenty of time. We are running a bit behind ourselves."

The Imagination cruised south down the west coast of Mexico, stopping at several ports for shopping, tours, and activities. My favorite turned out to be the Veranos zip-line, 35 miles outside Mazatlan, that Dalia convinced me to try.

"You have skied before, right?" she asked. "Well, a zip line is safer, warmer, and not half as scary as plunging down a snowy mountain on two fiberglass sticks."

On a ledge overlooking the forest canopy, I was outfitted with a body harness that they clipped onto a cable before giving me a gentle push. I soared across the rain forest, skimming over the canopy of lush, green trees with a spectacular bird's eye view. The white-water rapids below seemed challenging even from this height. Flying through the air gifted me a delicious freedom, feeling separate from my poor, ravaged body. I was unencumbered and unaffected, never having experienced such liberation. I wanted to stay suspended forever.

As has become accepted practice on every cruise, the infamous gourmet cuisine tended to destroy all self-control one had before boarding. Mickey stuffed himself at dinner, and then we excused him as he headed for the casino, not returning until nearly midnight. As he rejoined us and kissed me hello, we were surprised by a horde of people hurrying by in the opposite direction.

"Let's see where they are going," the four of us said in a simultaneous chorus.

We fell in with the crowd eventually finding ourselves front and center before a lavish table seducing us with a decadent array of desserts crafted by artists — wildly decorated triangles of cakes, dozens of assorted French pastries, creamy mousses, boozy flaming fruit, chocolate fountains, homemade ice cream, and a myriad of other nameless gourmet delicacies. It was futile to think we could satisfy our fantasies and sample each one, momentarily sticking us in the giddy stress of not being able to choose — until we saw the crowd descending on the table. We gobbled, savored, and relished every intoxicating bite, climaxing our finger-licking adventure riding high on a wide-eyed, sugar insomnia.

As the ship arrived back into port at San Diego, Mickey took me aside handing me a sweet little jewelry box. "I made a little money in the ship casino and next door was a tiny jewelry shop where I found this ideal memento to express my love and appreciation for you."

Inside I found the most precious, delicate bracelet. "Mickey, it is the perfect gift to a perfect end to a perfect vacation."

I held tightly to my sublime memories from the Carnival Imagination as the day of my first surgery quickly approached. I also held tightly to my new bracelet like a Catholic rosary, praying for a miracle.

37

SIX MONTHS LATER, I let myself into Maamaan's apartment, wondering why she had not come to check on me as she routinely did each morning. I entered her living room and found her sleeping in her favorite lounge chair, but as I got closer, I began to panic, realizing she was not sleeping. Death was in the room. I gently touched her arm, confirming my worst suspicions. Shame washed over me for not having paid more attention, always so consumed with my own impending death, never once cognizant that anything was wrong.

The next day, since our tradition requires a hasty burial, we interred her alongside my father. At the funeral service, I made a feeble attempt to concentrate on the heartfelt remarks from family and friends, but I was submerged in sorrow. The overwhelming reality that she was gone surpassed the accepted formalities and I grieved alone even though my family surrounded me.

I fell into a profound despair, not fully realizing while she was with us, how much stability she provided the family. She had served as the stable point around which we all revolved. How I wished I had told her how much I loved and respected her, but now that was never to be.

Sara Shirazi was an extremely strong and wise woman who, over her lifetime, had many impossible decisions to make under unthinkable circumstances and yet she never complained. Her quiet kindness was something to emulate.

When I told her I had cancer, she did not break down; she did not look at me with pity. Instead, she took my hands and looking directly at me said, "You do not realize your strength. You are one of the most courageous people I know, prevailing over many losses in your life. You conquered deafness. You stood up to oppression. You survived being uprooted from everything you knew. You fearlessly embraced a new culture. You learned English faster and better than anyone in the family. You withstood a miserable marriage and the loss of a baby with dignity. And you found Mickey. You will be fine."

But I was not to be fine. We were well tutored in the low percentages and statistics of surviving more than five years with my type of cancer. After having withstood four years of treatment with negligible results, my future had become bitterly clear, and Dr. Chung's face confirmed my suspicions.

My white blood cells had spiraled out of control, "Zhila, the chemotherapy is not giving us the results we were hoping for and is no longer a viable option, but I am not ready to give up yet. We have had slight success with an oral chemo, although I cannot promise anything. If you are willing, I would like to try it."

"We have come this far, it would make no sense to quit before exhausting your arsenal," I said.

The following day, I took the pill, realizing for better or worse, this little capsule held elation or despair. By the afternoon, I felt 100 percent confident that this pill was going to kill me. Just when you decide things cannot possibly get worse, you realize things can always get worse.

By evening, my symptoms had become so grim that I blacked out. Mickey found me collapsed on the bathroom floor and called paramedics and I awoke in the emergency room. The ER got me back on my feet, but the results were obvious — no more instant death pills for me.

We kept our appointment with Dr. Chung, even though we already knew we were starting the final chapter. He had read the hospital report from my episode and acknowledged there was nothing more he could do; his medicine cabinet was empty.

"How long?" Mickey asked.

"Perhaps three months, maybe more. Each individual is unique, and it is impossible to assign exact time, of course, but that is the question that everyone wants answered. I can only advise you to get your affairs in order and enjoy the time you have left surrounded by the people you love, engaging in the things that make you happy."

The only thing I could consider engaging in right now was a delicious Sleeping Beauty nap. Three days passed and, when I awoke, I felt stronger and better than I had in years. Perhaps the killer pill had produced a miracle after all?

Getting my affairs in order seemed simple enough. I let Goli know the impending situation and that I would not be able to visit her in Hawaii, so if she wanted to see me before I became worm food, she would have to come here. It seemed I had developed somewhat of a sense of humor about it all. Maybe that is *acceptance*. I assured her that I knew it could be an awkward visit, since I did not know what people talked about when they are preparing for death. I reassured her that I would understand if she would rather not come. This process of "*getting your affairs in order*" made me fully appreciate Maamaan's unplanned demise.

Two weeks later, Goli and I fell back quickly into the easy comfort of our years-long friendship. "Hawaii has been good to you. You cannot possibly be sixty-six. I am so jealous! Mr. Chemo has made me old and tired way beyond my years."

Goli laughed with me and lovingly squeezed my hand. "I was so sorry to hear about you mother. She was an outstanding woman."

"Yes, she really was. I have realized just how outstanding since she's been gone. She was really the rock of our family. Speaking of family, how is Cassie?"

"I'm flying to Houston to see her when I leave here. Why don't you come with me? She and her husband have a huge Texas spread. Come and experience the renowned southern hospitality. I don't even have to ask them; there is no doubt they will welcome you and Mickey like family. Texas is a very friendly place."

"Why not? My doctor told me to do what I love and spend time with people I love and I have nowhere else to be."

Early the next week, Mickey and I were on a flight to Houston. One of the unexpected benefits of my terminal diagnosis was the disappearance of my anxiety and depression. My outcome was already decided, so I had nothing to worry about or stress over. I was excited to see Goli's daughter again and meet her family.

I had always conceived Texans to be bible-thumping, Jew-hating Christians, although I could not imagine any daughter of Goli's having that mindset. I was right about Cassie, and so completely wrong about Texans. The people were extremely friendly and hospitable and nowhere had I ever felt more welcomed and comfortable. Every person should have the opportunity to personally experience southern hospitality. It cannot be described; it must be felt.

Cassie had a nanny for her three young children, and a staff to manage the house, but never did I feel they flaunted their wealth. They had made a beautiful life for themselves, and had opened their home to us as if we were family. Dr. Chung was right: this was the best kind of therapy, and I was so pleased to have spent this valuable time in a beautiful place with beautiful people, especially knowing this would be our final farewell.

Before leaving, we took advantage of visiting Space Center Houston, a science and space exploration center, to satisfy Mickey's education obsession. We spent extra time at the Mission Mars exhibit, experiencing a virtual Martian sunset. The simple irony of the exhibit struck me: we have the technology to explore the universe, send astronauts into space, maybe even Mars one day, but are completely ineffective in our ability to cure cancer, the scourge that randomly destroys life.

38

I HAD PICKED UP MICKEY'S HABIT of looking up random information and discovered "*hospice*" was a fourth-century Christian custom of caring for the ill. My doctor arranged for in-home hospice care for me, so it seemed I would be in the safe guardianship of a very long tradition.

I preferred Mickey not spend nights at my apartment, trying to shield him from the ugly parts of dying. Call it vanity, perhaps, but I could not abide having his memories of me obscured by visions of the noxious sewage and emissions that a body can produce. I chose to preserve the short time we had left with a modicum of dignity intact, and spare him the misery of dealing with unexpected occurrences. He begrudgingly agreed to spend only days with me instead.

As is the life of a cancer victim, I had good days, bad days, and horrible days — reminiscent of advice I had given Ziggy as an eleven-year-old boy sitting in an apple tree. I took advantage of my good days to examine and separate the assorted remnants and treasures I had collected that had sustained my existence. My life had been fairly simple, lacking any complex financials, so I spent most of my time on mundane tasks — cleaning out closets, giving away my belongings, writing letters to loved ones, and making time for friends and family.

Aunt Sabre came regularly, bearing her nourishing chicken soup, which was about the only thing I could manage to eat. She chatted about Parry and Joe's lives while we folded laundry and sorted through drawers of my junk. My siblings and their families visited as often as they could, which helped ease the angst and the unknowns of facing death, sometimes making it seem almost normal.

Time was my most valuable commodity and simple moments became especially poignant. One particular Sunday, Mickey and I spent the entire day with family — his and mine. Mickey and I laughed out loud at the Tower of Babel we had assembled on the patio. The simultaneous mix of Hebrew, Farsi, Sign Language, English, and baby babble was the sweetest scene, lifting me and infusing my heart with happiness.

Mickey brought us a movie to watch one afternoon and, while making popcorn he brought up Rebecca. "She came to see me yesterday."

She and Schmuel were living most of the year in California so they could be nearer to grandchildren and when needing a break, off they went back to their Florida hideaway. She had mellowed for some reason, so she and Mickey seemed to be getting along better.

"What did she want?"

"I must say I was suspicious at first when she started off thanking me for being such a great father. I kept waiting for the other shoe to drop, but then she went on to elaborate on what a good job I had done with Aviva and Dalia. Imagine that?"

When I clapped my hands, Mickey said, "Wait, there's more. She said she wanted to reduce my financial worries to ease my retirement, and offered to buy me a condo — an investment for her. I just have to pay the monthly Home Owner Association fees. Why do you think she would do that?"

"Well, you raised the girls so that she could concentrate on starting her business — that made millions. She knew you were a great father and would never have to worry about the girls. You gave her everything she wanted in the divorce and generous spousal support without a fight. You even paid child support for the insignificant time she actually took care of them. Guilt maybe? Or maybe she actually has a heart and realized it was time to be fair. Honestly, I don't care about her motives, I am just happy that you will not have to worry so much about money."

Mickey hired his friend Suzy, as his realtor, a slender woman in her mid-forties who he had met in his writing group. She was a good communicator, so he felt confident that she would be the perfect person to help him find what he wanted. Within a couple weeks, he found a place on the third floor, coincidentally across the street from my apartment.

The cancer was devouring the cells of my body as if it were creating a new entity that was pushing me out, so I rarely left the apartment. Nights were still difficult, and I still stubbornly refused to allow Mickey to stay the night. Despite the logical case he presented, I was uncompromising on the subject.

I knew time had run out, and my death was imminent, the evening that I began having trouble swallowing. That meant that the two things allowing me to die at home — pain meds and chicken soup — were no longer an option. I awoke in a panic, short of breath with blurred vision and called 911, also texting Mickey, knowing he likely would not get it until morning.

I was admitted to the hospital, and they resolved my immediate symptoms and injected me with something marvelous that knocked me out. When I awoke, Mickey was sleeping in a chair next to the bed.

He came daily to the hospital as the alien cancer invaded, taking over what was left of my deteriorated body. Gone were my long dark tresses, replaced with snowy white; my sunken cheeks had been sculpted into an unrecognizable corpse. I was wholly ready to shed this shell and venture into the unknown. Drifting back to painful consciousness, I asked the nurse to please find Mickey before my next dose of medication.

• • •

"Zhila is asking for you before I give her more meds," the nurse said with concern on her face.

Mickey understood the implication of that statement, taking a deep breath and steeling himself before entering the room. He yearned to wind back time to devise a magical repair to change the ending of the story. She looked weaker than she had a half hour ago, and so utterly vulnerable. He took her hand and she smiled, but could no longer hide the anguish in her eyes.

"Mickey," she said slowly, too weak to sign, "I want you to know I am glad you encouraged me not to give up. I want you to know it was worth it, so no guilt, okay? I wish I could properly convey my profound gratitude. I never knew I could love so deeply. You have taught me so much, and made my life full and rich. I have only one request: that you ensure my precious bracelet remains around my wrist after I pass. It will give me security for whatever is to come next."

"I promise. You have been so fearless and courageous throughout this ordeal. I know it was intolerable, yet you indulged my selfishness while being selfless. It was you who taught me, and I will always remember your generosity and will honor you by paying it forward. You will always be the shining jewel of my life."

They held up *I love you* signs and held their hands pressed together.

Two hours later, Zhila Shirazi cast off her body and silently slipped away.

Addendum

When Aviva gave birth to our first grandchild, Faye, I was dubbed *Papa* and Zhila was *Nana*. When *Nana* died, Faye was three years old.

My hearing aids could not help to decipher three-year old babble at all, so I rarely had any idea what she was saying. But she never noticed, and we were always able to pretend and imagine together despite my deafness.

Two weeks after Zhila passed, I sat playing with Faye on the floor in her room. I was in a fog, drowning in despair, barely present, just going through the motions of our game.

Suddenly, Faye stopped playing, tapped me to get my withered attention, and said in a slow and distinct voice, "Nana is happy now."

Five years of accumulated emotion was unleashed, surging out of me, forcing me to leave the room so not to scare my little messenger. The catharsis was transformative, cleansing all the stuck points of *what if, why,* and *I wish*, and thus I began my healing.

I have no doubt that my innocent granddaughter became a vehicle for God to send the message that Zhila was okay. The coerced disconnect from my cherished love, intensified by the uncertainty of her disposition, had trapped me in a deep depression. And then, through a magical convergence of God, a guileless child provided certainty that Zhila was okay. No more pain, no more fear, no longer trapped in a useless body.

Zhila had an enormous heart. If she had but one shirt to wear and you had none, she would give you hers. Every year, she would mourn for Christmas trees as if they were mortal. She viewed this as a despicable custom that completely bewildered her and would cry for these gifts of nature, cut down and trapped on a lot, only to be erected in homes and then discarded on the street to be collected as trash. When she found herself surrounded by children begging in the streets of Mexico, it pained her to the bone to witness the result of the greed of corrupt, soulless humans. How could they allow this appalling disgrace to befall these innocents when they had all the resources to easily prevent it? This scene would send Zhila spiraling into depression. I have no doubt that her inability to harden herself against these inhumanities from a civilization as seemingly advanced as ours, contributed to her early death.

The concept of a saint does not exist in Judaism. Instead, we honor *Tzadikim*, meaning *righteous ones*. It is said that every generation gives rise to at least thirty-six *Tzadikim*, and through them our world receives the divine vitality that pushes it forward and away from the abyss. I always felt certain that Zhila was a *Tzadikim*, paving a righteous path toward love, honesty, and justice. Her simplicity and compassion are permanently etched on my heart, becoming a sacred part of me.

To honor her memory, I ask that if you pass a homeless person on the street and wonder how you can help, donate to a charity in memory of Zhila that supports these displaced citizens. If you have items to dispose of, donate to Goodwill, Zhila's favorite charity.

And if you go to the park, take plenty of breadcrumbs for the birds and tell them, "These are from Zhila-joon."

About the Author

Michael Thal is a freelance writer and author in Los Angeles, California. Michael began his career in public education, but due to a severe hearing loss, he left his tenured sixth grade teaching assignment to learn the writing craft.

Michael has written over 80 articles for magazines like *Highlights For Children*, *Fun for Kidz*, *Writer's Digest*, and *San Diego Family Magazine*. His novels include *Goodbye Tchaikovsky*, *The Legend of Koolura*, *Koolura and the Mystery at Camp Saddleback*, *Koolura and the Mayans*, and *The Abduction of Joshua Bloom*.

You can learn more about Michael and his works at *michaelthal.com*.

Made in the USA
Columbia, SC
14 November 2021

48953784R00145